First published in Great Britain in 2004
By Brignell Associates

ISBN: 0-9539108-2-2

Cover picture by Barry Diaper

Printing by PrintingData.com 0870 444 6159
www.printingdata.com

Time Chart

2000 BC	Purification and filtration of water in the Middle East
460 BC	Birth of Hippocrates, the father of medicine
410 BC	Book I of *The Epidemics*
300 BC	Roman aqueducts
19 BC	Pont du Gard begun
129	Birth of Galen
1214	Birth of Roger Bacon
1333	Outbreak of Black Death in China
1350	Black Death spreads across Europe and reaches Iceland
1493	Birth of Auroleus Phillipus Theostratus Bombastus von Hohenheim, alias "Paracelsus"
1514	Birth of Vesalius
1530	Girolamo Fracastoro states the germ theory and founds epidemiology
1561	Birth of Francis Bacon
1578	Birth of William Harvey
1636	Foundation of Harvard College
1665	The Great Plague devastates London
1683	Antonie van Leeuwenhoek observes "animalcules"
1720	Benjamin Marten conjectures in *A New Theory of Consumption* that TB could be caused by "wonderfully minute living creatures".
1782	Foundation of Harvard Medical School
1796	Edward Jenner inoculates with cowpox to prevent smallpox – the first immunisation
1822	Birth of Louis Pasteur
1831	Cholera enters Britain
1842	The Chadwick report
1848	The first Public Health Act
1849	John Snow's cholera pamphlet
1854	John Snow and the Broad Street pump
1855	Florence Nightingale demonstrates statistically the dominance of disease in war deaths
1858	The Great Stench of London
1860	Pasteur disproves spontaneous generation
1865	Jean-Antoine Villemin demonstrates consumption passed from humans to cattle and from cattle to rabbits
1869	Joseph Lister introduces antiseptic surgery
1872	Ferdinand Cohn establishes bacteriology
1874	Discovery of DDT
1875	The Public Health Act
1882	Robert Koch isolates tubercle bacillus
1883	Cholera bacillus identified
1885	First inoculation for rabies by Louis Pasteur
1890	Chlorination of water
1895	Discovery of radiation by Roentgen
1894	Last great plague pandemic starts in China. Plague bacterium discovered. Diphtheria antitoxin developed.
1897	First vaccine against typhus
1912	Fisher's first publication
1922	Foundation of Harvard School of Public Health
1924	BCG vaccine for tuberculosis introduced
1929	Fleming discovers antibiotic properties of penicillin
1939	Insecticidal properties of DDT identified
1944	Discovery of streptomycin. Antibiotic treatment of TB
1945	Orwell's *Animal Farm*
1948	Annual malaria rate in Sri Lanka reaches 2.8 million
1949	Orwell's *Nineteen eighty-four*
1954	Salk introduces first polio vaccine
1962	Publication of *Silent Spring* by Rachel Carson
1963	DDT reduces annual malaria rate in Sri Lanka to 17
1964	DDT banned in Sri Lanka
1965	Bradford Hill's criteria
1967	WHO launches world-wide vaccination campaign against smallpox, which causes 2 million deaths per year
1969	Annual malaria rate in Sri Lanka reaches 2.5 million. Man steps onto the moon
1970	Foundation of the Environmental Protection Agency
1971	Nixon declares War Against Cancer
1977	Last reported case of smallpox
1979	McKeown launches the Social Theory in *The Role of Medicine*
1988	McKeown launches the new epidemiology with *The Origins of Human Disease*
1991	Cholera outbreak in Peru kills 6,000. Greenpeace declares war on chlorine
1992	EPA risk assessment on Environmental Tobacco Smoke (ETS)
1993	Carol Browner appointed EPA Administrator. EPA claims 3,000 deaths a year from passive smoking
1996	WHO reports a new epidemic of tuberculosis
2000	Le Fanu publishes *Rise and fall of modern medicine*
2001	Foot and mouth disease and the slaughter of 8 million British farm animals
2004	BMA's Orwellian rewrite of the Bradford Hill criteria

The Epidemiologists:
Have they got scares for you!

By John Brignell

This book is dedicated to James Le Fanu.
Many look, few see.

It seems to me that one of the prime jobs of every educated man on this earth is to denounce charlatans. New ones are always popping up, and the common run of idiots are always succumbing to them. There is little if any difference between one and another.

H L Mencken

Contents

1. Introduction

There are two sorts of statistics, those you look up and those you make up.
Death of a doxy – Rex Stout

A headline from *The Independent*, June 5th, 2001:
Pets 'double children's risk of asthma attacks'

And another from the BBC a few days earlier, May 27th:
Keeping pets 'prevents allergies'

The astonishing thing about these headlines is the fact that they passed without remark. **Hormone Studies: What Went Wrong?** "How could two large high-quality studies come to diametrically different conclusions about menopause, hormone therapy and heart disease?" lamented the *New York Times* in April 2003. Earlier the same month **Pain killers prevent cancer** provided the giant headlines; yet in September 1999 it had been **Regular pain killer use linked to cancer**. By January 2004 it was **Aspirin linked with 30% increase in cancer**. Or how about **Soy sauce cancer warning** from the Food Standards Agency in June 2001 followed five months later by **Another Study Showing Soy Fights Cancer** from the University of Missouri?

It was just "the scientists" contradicting each other again. The public had become totally blasé about it. One moment some substance, say coffee or soya, caused cancer and the next it cured it. Science had fallen into total disrepute. It was producing scares and breakthroughs on a daily basis and then demolishing them a few days later. In October 2001, asymmetry of the fingers was the clue to potential heart disease in men. By November, fingers were out and legs were in and it was short-legged men who were in danger. A year later fingers returned, but only if they were arthritic. Science had always had its disputes and had come to tolerate ambiguities (such as the wave-particle duality) but this was something different. Statements were being made in the name of science and then almost immediately contradicted. It went further than that. Vast industries had been set up on the basis of insubstantial "scientific facts" such as "bad cholesterol" in the diet caused heart disease, while "good cholesterol" did not. It was not simply the contradictions. Statements were frequently made in the media, quoting the authority of "the scientists", which were patently absurd to the ordinary punter with a modicum of intelligence. Left-handed people were twice as likely to get bowel disease. Twins were 20% less likely to get cancer. Anorexics were more likely to be born in June. The list of everyday substances that were claimed to be "carcinogenic" grew day by day, including bizarre additions such as church incense. Doom laden headlines such as **Chips and crisps linked to cancer** are greeted with hilarity in pubs and clubs, as indeed are "breakthroughs" such as **White wine improves lung function**. Yet the media keep trotting them out with solemn ceremony.

HRT: Who can you believe? wailed the *Daily Mail* in a giant banner headline in April 2004. In the preceding two years HRT had been "linked with" breast cancer, heart attacks, strokes and Alzheimer's. Suddenly, when more than half the women taking the therapy had abandoned it, hundreds of thousands of them, an American study announced that all the previous claims had been exaggerated.

After a couple of centuries in which science, representing the triumph of reason, had revolutionised human life and tripled life-span, it was now reduced to the status of necromancy or astrology. Ordinary people paid more regard to what their "stars" had to say than what the "scientists" did. Yet science was much the same as it had always been, apart from the exponential growth of knowledge, and it had maintained the rigour of what was known as the scientific method. Best of all it had delivered. People were far healthier, wealthier and longer living than could have been conceived in earlier centuries, and it was all due to science. Nevertheless a canker had been gnawing at its vitals. It was a complex disease, nurtured by politics, bureaucracy, media populism and corporate venality. Many branches of science were afflicted, climatology being particularly notable, but one stood out in its readiness to yield to the embrace of populism, and that was epidemiology, which is why a humble academic engineer came to find himself writing a book about a branch of medicine.

It started as an itch that just had to be scratched. I had devoted my professional life to the subject of measurement, beginning with my apprenticeship in avionics. It was something whose integrity I felt was of the utmost importance to human society. Yet, as the millennium came to a close, every morning when I opened my newspaper I found blatant examples of its abuse. I just had to write a book about it to get it off my chest. As I researched the subject I began to discover a systematic lying on a grand scale, reaching into the upper strata of our society. It began to consume my very existence and finally I took early retirement from my chair in Industrial Instrumentation in order to complete my opus, which finally emerged as a book I called *Sorry, wrong number!*

It is one of the trials of life that as soon as you get rid of one itch another replaces it. In my case it was the mystery of how one branch of science seemed to have become a corrupt travesty; and it was not just any branch of science, but one that had been of immense importance to human welfare from its inception. So I began to research something that is almost as remote from my own discipline of electronics as you can get. Of course, I was not alone in my concern. There were other voices crying in the wilderness, but they seemed to be ignored by the politicians and media who rule our lives.

As the story unfolded there were further enigmas. How, for example, the very people (and one in particular) who sought to introduce rigour into the subject inadvertently provided the means of its corruption. How the humane impulse to eliminate the fear of terrible diseases from our society became twisted to produce even more fears, and ones of an imaginary and fantastical nature, that had people all over the world conducting their lives in irrational ways. How chimeras summoned up by the few were used to enslave the many and trap them in pointless rituals of taboo, which reduced them to the fearful state of their primitive ancestors. Less mysterious and more predictable was the fact that a lot of people made a lot of money out of the whole shooting match. A whole new caste of witch doctors, Machiavellian princes and media gurus arose to exploit the situation and feather their own nests. Worst of all, a science that grew out of a desire to save human (and animal) lives began to destroy them on a grand scale.

I needed to find out how it all began; when and why it started to go wrong; who were the villains and heroes of the piece. The results of my investigations are presented in what follows.

This book is by its very nature a sequel. In order to make it self contained, a certain amount of material from *Sorry, wrong number!* has been repeated, though in a highly abbreviated form. Where references are made to the earlier book, they are in the form (*Sorry, Chapter X*). Some of the material has also been developed on the author's web site, *Number Watch*, and a great deal is owed to the many correspondents from all over the world who have contributed ideas and information.

The people featured in this book are not all formally epidemiologists, but they share certain characteristics with the worst of them, particularly in their approach to scientific evidence. Nor are all epidemiologists tarred with the same brush and there were some (at Yale, for instance) who had adopted a wholly rigorous and proper approach. Nor are epidemiologists always the bad guys. The MMR vaccine scare, for example, was drummed up by a renegade medical researcher and it was the epidemiologists who provided the solid evidence to refute it, not that that stopped the media exploiters from keeping it going, thereby exposing a generation of children to unwarranted risks.

The early chapters of this book are concerned with the historical origins of the subject, starting with the terrible toll disease has inflicted on mankind through the ages. Then comes a great breakthrough with the tale of the Broad Street Pump, which brought into focus centuries of slow convergence on an understanding of the nature of disease. There follows an abbreviated account of the work of one of the great pioneers of statistics and the dramatic irony of his legacy. Then comes the Social Theory, which turned scientific medicine on its head and changed the world. A brief discussion of the fraught subject of cause and effect completes the preparatory half of the book.

The second half of the book represents the results of a struggle to cope with the overwhelming amount of available material. Two chapters deal with the basics of how the present situation came about, tools of the trade and fallacies. There follows an exercise in critical reading in epidemiology, which takes one random example from the media coverage and picks over its bones. The following three chapters are devoted to a small selection of examples divided arbitrarily into trials of life, body parts and substance abuse. Then, because of the unique way in which its history is tied in with modern epidemiology, tobacco receives a chapter of its own, as does cancer, the ultimate scare. There follows a chapter on the history of a holocaust in which millions of animals were needlessly slaughtered. Next is a survey of some of the delights and disasters associated with electromagnetic fields. The penultimate chapter lists some of the big players in the scare game and the final chapter ties up a few loose ends.

Acknowledgements

Many individuals have made contributions of various kinds to the work that led up to this book; questions, suggestions, criticisms and even financial support. Outstanding has been Simon Scott, whose contributions on all fronts were way beyond the call of duty. Jaime Arbona also offered considerable assistance in the preparation of the text. Other number watchers who contributed were Bill Adams, Dennis Ambler, John Baltutis, Brian Baker, David Barron, Nick Barron, Bob Bateman, Axel Berger, Steve Binder, Tim Boettcher, Frank Borger, Alan Caruba, Alwyn Davies, David Delany, Stephen Dillon, Matt DiMeo, Andrew Duffin, Dennis Falgout, Ray Futtrel, Andrew Gilchrist, Peter Hattingh, Andy Hodginson, Barry Holland, Robert Hookway, Peter Hope, Colin Hunt, Mathew Iredale, Neil Johnston, Angela Kelly, Bill Kinney, John Lichtenstein, Rob Lyons, Aaron Oakley, Tony Ridgway, Miceal O'Ronain, Paul Oxley, Claude Perron, Paul Power, Al Pratt, Grant Perk, Donal Ragan, Ian Reid, Theresa Rice, Philip Stott, Michael Thomas, Brad Tittle, Van Varney and Adrian Watson. Much thanks to all of them.

2. A past of plague and pestilence

Diseases desperate grown,
By desperate appliances are reliev'd,
Or not at all.
Hamlet

Thanks to scientific medicine, modern man is unique in the history of the world in being almost unaffected by infectious disease. Until quite recently most families had the tragic experience of prematurely losing their loved ones, often in infancy.

It is difficult to comprehend now, but the whole course of human history has been largely determined by infectious disease. Great armies have been defeated not by opposing forces but by debilitating and often fatal illnesses. Alexander the Great, the most notable conqueror in history, contracted a fever and was struck down a young man, while at the height of his powers and achievements. Henry V's triumphant progress after Harfleur and Agincourt was brought to a halt by sickness among his diminished force. Henry himself fell ill and died at the age of only 35, which led to the chaos of the Wars of the Roses. In the Crimean War far more soldiers died from disease than in battle. Florence Nightingale showed that deaths in the British field hospitals reached a peak during January 1855, when 2,761 soldiers died of contagious diseases, 83 from wounds and 324 from other causes making a total of 3,168. The army's average manpower for that month was 32,393. Using this information, she computed an annual mortality rate of 1,174 per 1,000 with 1,023 per 1,000 being from zymotic diseases. If this rate had continued, and troops had not been replaced frequently, then disease alone would have killed the entire British army in the Crimea. For much of the remainder of her life Florence was bedridden, owing to an illness contracted in the Crimea, which prevented her from continuing her own work as a nurse, but she had made original contributions to applied statistics.

In the Great War of 1914 more people expired of 'flu than from the war, 20 million of them. There are many myths concerning the influence of disease on the built heritage around us (for example, that the wonderful perpendicular style of architecture was a result of the shortage of masons after the Black Death) but it is indisputable that many great migrations and political catastrophes were caused by disease. The Irish famine was precipitated by a plant disease, blight, but its effects were compounded by the spread of Asiatic cholera. It is indisputable that infectious disease has been a controlling factor in human development. Yet by the last quarter of the twentieth century it seemed to have been conquered (at least as far as the western world was concerned) and a thing of the past.

Let us survey briefly some of the most important of these diseases.

Bubonic plague

"...it would rush upon its victims with the speed of a fire racing through dry or oily substances that happened to be placed within its reach."
Giovanni Boccaccio on the Black Death (mid-1300's)

On July 11th 1563 in Stratford upon Avon, John Bretchgirdle buried one Oliver Gunn, a weaver's apprentice, and after the entry in the register wrote the ominous words *hic incipit pestis,* "here begins the plague". Bretchgirdle is only noteworthy because the following year on April 26th he christened the child William and entered *Guliemus filius Johannes Shakspere.* In the first half of 1563 there had been twenty-two burials. In the second half there were two hundred and thirty seven. William's baby sister Margaret died that year, as did many of their neighbours. Whole families perished. Survival was a lottery and the world was fortunate that little William was one of the winners.

Plague was a rather vague term given to a variety of epidemic infectious diseases, but the most dramatic of them was the Black Death or bubonic plague. The sixteenth century occurrence was one of many outbreaks, from the Black Death of the fourteenth century to the great Plague of 1665. The Black Death began with an outbreak in China in 1333 and over the next decade and a half it moved remorselessly westward, carried by merchants, pilgrims and other travellers along the established land and sea trade routes. It reached Constantinople in 1347, Messina in Sicily in October 1347, and Paris and the south coast of England in the summer of 1348. By 1350 it had covered most of Europe and reached as far as Iceland and Greenland. There were further outbreaks over the years, but in the final flourish the Great Plague of London (1664-1666) killed more people than any other epidemic, with approximately 68,500 burials of plague victims being recorded during its 18-month course.

The impact of the Black Death was profound, and it brought many social and economic changes. Land became less scarce, while labour became more expensive. After a few sporadic outbreaks, such as Marseille in 1720, the incidence of plague declined. Perhaps humanity had developed some immunity, but improved hygiene must have had an effect and the black rat was largely replaced by the brown rat. For as we now all know, the plague is carried by the black rat and transmitted by its flea, *Xenopsylla cheopis.* We should note that it is not undisputed that the Black Death was in fact bubonic plague and some authorities believe that it was more likely to have been a virus disease like Ebola.

As in the case of malaria, many believed that the cause was corruption of the air by an invisible but deadly miasma emerging from the ground, hence its name, and suggested that recent earthquakes had released unhealthy vapours long trapped underground. Bad smells, a prevalent feature of medieval life, were also blamed; so popular remedies included the carrying of sweet-smelling nosegays. Indeed, open sewers, insanitary housing, middens, butchers' shambles, and stinking ditches were common. The elimination of these hazards by the encouragement of better hygiene and sanitation, prompt burial of the victims in overflow cemeteries ("plague pits") outside the city walls; and the burning of their clothing all went to improve general health. Ironically, even the exotic New World habit of smoking of tobacco was thought effective as a prophylactic.

The church, and moralists generally, preached that the Black Death was a punishment from God for the sins of mankind, and called for a moral regeneration of society. Immoderate eating and drinking, immoral sexual behaviour, and luxurious living were all to blame. Naturally at such times, congregations swelled.

In a more sinister, yet sadly familiar, movement, the usual outcasts of society were picked on. Beggars and the very poor were accused of contaminating ordinary folk. Where the Jews were once tolerated, popular fury turned against them. In some West German and Swiss cities there was a widespread massacre of Jews, who were accused of poisoning the wells, a crime to which many confessed under torture. The search for culprits was a godsend to the Single Issue Fanatics (SIFs) of the day, much as it is now.

Malaria

Varieties of the genus of protozoon known as *plasmodium* are parasitic in a number of animals. They are carried by over sixty different varieties of the mosquito *anopheles*. Four of the forms of the parasite afflict human beings, constitute one of the great threats to human life and probably account for more deaths than any other cause. Throughout the world there are 100 million new cases every year and one percent of them lead to death. There have been, and still are, many myths about malaria. Its very name derives from the belief that it was caused by "bad air". It is not just a tropical disease, but has been known in regions as far north as the Arctic Circle. St Petersburg became known as the city built on bones, after over 100,000 men died from malaria while building it. The recrudescence of malaria has been one of the most tragic scandals of the modern age, a matter to which we must return later.

Smallpox

This was an acute and highly contagious disease. After a 12-day incubation period, the first symptoms were a high fever, chills, backaches, and headaches, followed three or four days later by a rash, characteristically on the face, the palms, the back and the soles of the feet. During the next few days the rash developed into blister-like pustules, which could become secondarily infected by bacteria. Death occurred if the virus attacked the vital organs. Eventually the pustules split and dried, leaving the characteristic pock-marked appearance that is now familiar only to the older generation.

Until the 18th century smallpox was a major cause of death throughout the world, but Edward Jenner (1749-1823) observed that those who had been infected with the milder disease of cowpox became immune. He was thus able to begin the process of immunisation and led the way to the founding of immunology by Louis Pasteur. It was not until 1967 that the WHO initiated a worldwide vaccination programme that finally eliminated the disease.

Diphtheria

Children were particularly prone to this acute and highly infectious disease, which was a major cause of child death until an antitoxin was developed in 1894. Until then mortality had been as high as 90%, but it fell to 5%. Eventually immunisation was developed in the form of toxoids that produced immunity when given to infants in their first year.

Influenza

The flu or *la grippe* is a potentially serious disease that has lost some of its horror through sheer familiarity. There have been over thirty major pandemics since it was first recorded in the sixteenth century, the worst being in 1918 when it caused over 20 million deaths. It is widely regarded as little more than a serious form of the common cold, which is in fact the symptom of over a hundred different virus infections. Influenza, however, is caused by three distinct groups of virus, which exhibit remarkable powers of mutation. Thus, while it is preventable by vaccination, the development of appropriate vaccines is dependent upon a global early warning system. The great danger of flu is that it weakens the immune system, so that serious illness and death are often produced by secondary bacterial infections. The threat of a serious outbreak is ever present. The world relies on a relatively small group of medics to determine correctly each year which are the currently dangerous strains, so that vaccination programmes can be designed accordingly. The consequences of a miscalculation could be calamitous.

Tuberculosis

This was and is a worldwide problem. It is dealt with in some detail in our later chapter 5 on the Social Theory.

Typhus and Typhoid

Typhus and typhoid fever are actually two different diseases, which are often confused and were not differentiated until 1837. They were known under various names, such as jail fever, camp fever and ship fever, as they were common where men were crowded together. Typhus is carried by body parasites. In World War I, 150,000 men died of it, but by the Second World War the miracle of DDT prevented a recurrence and eventually antibiotics largely diminished the threat.

In contrast, typhoid fever is a highly infectious bacterial disease, usually transmitted by the contamination of food and drink with the faeces of carriers, who are often themselves immune. It is now largely controlled by inoculation and treated with various antibiotics. Untreated it can progress to pneumonia, intestinal haemorrhage and death.

Whooping Cough

This is a disease caused by a bacillus that is particularly serious in very young children. It is highly infectious, being spread by droplets resulting from coughing, but is now largely controlled by immunisation. Now only the elderly remember the fear with which it was associated when they were children.

Hepatitis

A group of diseases affecting the liver are known as hepatitis, but they vary greatly in seriousness. The most potent is hepatitis B, which is spread by body fluids and causes a quarter of a million deaths a year worldwide. Hepatitis A is more infectious and tends to break out where people are crowded together in unsanitary conditions.

Cholera

This is a very serious disease that has caused huge numbers of deaths throughout history. It is the main subject of our next chapter.

Measles, Mumps and Rubella

These three highly contagious viral diseases are lumped together in common parlance because they are now effectively dealt with by a single combined vaccine administered in early childhood. Again only the elderly can remember the devastation that they caused and view with alarm the complacency with which they are now treated.

Measles, forgotten though it may be in the West, kills more than a million children round the world every year, over half of them in Africa. It is characterised by the well-known rash, but can invade organs such as the ears, lung and brain. In the days before vaccination and antibiotics for secondary infections it could result in deafness, blindness, pneumonia, meningitis and death. It still does where modern medicine is not available.

Mumps normally invades the parotid salivary glands, causing the characteristic swelling, but it can also infect the testes of adult or adolescent males with very unpleasant results, including infertility. Serious complications are more likely to occur in adults and can include meningitis, encephalitis, deafness and spontaneous abortions. A fifth of those infected show no symptoms but still spread the disease.

Rubella is normally a mild infection. Also known as German Measles, it is characterised by a skin rash. The main reason it is feared is that it can have a devastating effect on a developing foetus, but it can lead to bleeding disorders and encephalitis.

All three of these diseases could be eliminated from the world, like smallpox, if there were widespread vaccination. Ironically, because of a mischievous scare started by a few medical researchers and propagated by the media they are actually on the rise in the UK.

Of all these rightly feared diseases it was to be cholera that provoked thought and action in one medical practitioner, which was to lead to the foundation of modern epidemiology and its greatest triumph.

3. The Broad Street Pump

There is a reaper, whose name is death,
And with his sickle keen,
He reaps the bearded grain at a breath,
And the flowers that grow between.
Longfellow

Death in Soho

There is an unusual trophy exhibited in a London pub. The trophy is a pump handle and the pub is called the John Snow, being named after a London physician, noted in the mid-nineteenth century as an obstetrician and among the first to use anaesthesia. It was, however, to be in an entirely different field that Snow was to achieve fame and become the founding father of modern epidemiology.

The disease that posed the most serious threat in the nineteenth century was cholera, a very violent form of diarrhoea. It was believed to have entered Britain in 1831 through the port of Sunderland and it quickly spread throughout the country. It was particularly rampant in the larger towns. At that time there was no effective means of treatment and the death rate was very high.

Waves of cholera swept the western world at regular intervals. By the 1840s, London in particular was prey to severe epidemics and Snow had become interested in the cause and transmission of the disease. In 1849, he published a modest pamphlet, *On the Mode of Communication of Cholera*, suggesting that cholera is a contagious disease caused by a poison capable of reproducing in the human body and emerging in the vomit and faeces of sufferers. He believed that the most significant means of transmission was water contaminated with this poison. This differed from the then current orthodoxy that diseases are transmitted by inhalation of vapours. It was just one of many theories proposed at a time, when cholera was a source of great distress, and it went relatively unnoticed.

Snow, however, was not alone in his concern. Edwin Chadwick, a civil servant who had trained as a barrister and journalist, led a survey of the poor districts of London and in 1842 he published the *Report on the sanitary conditions of the labouring population*. He described the appalling conditions that existed and proposed drastic measures for changing them. Chadwick's Report was initially ignored by the government of the day, but in 1848 it passed the first Public Health Act. This delay was rather odd since Members of Parliament could not walk out on the balcony of the House in the summer months without holding scented handkerchiefs across their noses and mouths. In 1858 the work of Parliament was nearly brought to a standstill by what became known as the *Great Stench of London*.

Meanwhile, in 1854, Snow had the opportunity to test his theory in another massive outbreak of cholera. He made a study of all the cases in the Soho area of

London and discovered that almost all the victims had drunk water from the public water pump in Broad Street. He suggested that the pump handle be removed and when this was done people were forced to go elsewhere to obtain their water. The epidemic came to an end and it was later shown that the water in the well supplying the Broad Street pump had been contaminated by a cesspool serving houses in which a cholera patient had lived.

Snow's map of the Soho area (which as now was bounded by Regent Street, Oxford Street, Charing Cross Road and Shaftesbury Avenue) shows each death from cholera as bars and the pump as a circle. It does not need a great deal of sophisticated statistical analysis to see that the pump, in the middle of what is now known as Broadwick Street, is near the centroid of a genuine and large cluster of deaths. This does not, of course, provide any proof of causation, but the dramatic end to the epidemic is very substantial evidence indeed.

It was not until 1875 that a new Public Health Act forced local authorities to provide adequate drainage and sewage systems in their towns and a safe water supply.

Figure 3.1 Snow's map of Soho

The forgotten lessons of Dr Snow

It is a comparatively rare event in the history of science that one man makes an intuitive leap that alters the future. Some of the truly great geniuses, such as Newton and Einstein, did it many times. Although such events give birth to great complexities, they are usually in themselves based on extremely simple innovations. Snow's contribution ranks among these great leaps of inspiration, with the added merit that it was to save millions of lives. There were a number of far-reaching consequences of his simple conjecture and subsequent observation. Some of the more important of which were destined to be forgotten by many of his successors.

The proliferation of germs

One of Snow's most important insights was to recognise that the "poison" that caused cholera was capable of reproducing itself within the human body. He could have had little idea of just how prolific this poison could be. We now know that the generation time between bacterial cell divisions can be as little as twenty minutes, which means that one bacillus can become one million in under seven hours. Antonie van Leeuwenhoek of Delft had in fact observed "animalcules" in pond water nearly two centuries earlier, which he reported to the Royal Society of London in 1683. However, the compound microscope was yet to be invented and his observation was not to be reliably repeated until the mid-1880s. Louis Pasteur in 1860 was able to disprove the prevailing theory that bacteria generated spontaneously. The science of bacteriology was not established until 1872, when Ferdinand Cohn produced his treatise. Thus Snow was ahead of his time when he made his original conjecture.

Statistical inference

Snow's meticulously prepared map is also in itself simple in concept, yet one introducing ideas of great power and significance. The mathematical ideas of probability and statistics had already been established by the likes of Bernoulli, Gauss and Quételet. Mortality tables had also been long used (e.g. by the astronomer Edmund Halley in 1693). Nevertheless, Snow's simple illustration of a two dimensional distribution with the offending well more or less at its centroid, was a powerful innovation. His method was an exemplar of good science, proceeding from a hypothesis, through the gathering of evidence (the map), to a critical test (removal of the pump handle). He had a large number of data to produce evidence of a cluster, some 500 deaths. No doubt he would have been shocked if told that one day a mere half a dozen deaths, or even two, would be held to identify a significant cluster.

Cycles of consumption

It was not until the age of electronics that we began fully to understand the concept of feedback and the instabilities that could arise from it. If you connect a microphone to a loudspeaker via an amplifier it will work perfectly satisfactorily until you allow acoustic feedback to occur between the output and the input. We then get the familiar howl that occurs when the amateur orator waves his microphone about in front of the loudspeaker. In the jargon he has turned an open loop system into a closed loop one, which is capable of instability. The human body is an open loop system until excreta are allowed to enter the food chain. We use the word "chain" as a metaphor for the linear progression of nutriments from the most primitive organisms to the topmost predators, ourselves. It is basically a linear concept, but feedback turns it into a loop, which is capable of instability.

There is another requirement for the loop, once closed, to become unstable, which is that the loop gain has to be greater than one. Thus if one hundred bacteria at any point in Snow's closed loop produce an average of 101 when we trace them around the whole loop and back to the same point, we have the recipe for exponential growth. If they produce only 99 we have exponential decay and the system is stable. Snow's conjecture of the reproductive capability of the poison was equivalent to stating that the loop gain was greater than one and that infinite proliferation was a possibility.

It is a remarkable testament to the fallibility of humankind that a century later this truism had been forgotten. We began to feed the herbivores that were a major part of our diet with the remains of their own kind. Furthermore, for the sake of economy, we began to whittle away at the heat and chemical treatment that had made this foolish practice relatively safe. The result was the BSE disaster, of which more later, but it could have been almost anything.

Purification

The movement for pure drinking water was already well under way by Snow's time. In 1828 a Royal Commission recommended that sources for water supplies should be moved upstream and that suspended matter should be removed. These recommendations were based on aesthetic rather than health reasons but, as they were adopted, public health improved. In fact, stringent city regulations had controlled cesspools in the streets from the 14th century, and the disposal of offal and refuse was also subject to strict regulation. In the 17th century the New River Company had been formed to bring water in a canal along the edge of the Lea Valley to reservoirs in the City. Water was being pumped directly into people's homes.

Thus the Broad Street pump was something of an aberration, but only one of many, and it was only after the health hazards of impure water had been so dramatically demonstrated that there was real impetus behind the effort to ban contamination.

Britain and America had at last caught up with the ancient civilisations. Channelled water supplies had existed in the Middle East for over five thousand years, and purification by filtering had been practised in 2000 BC. The Romans were building aqueducts in 300 BC and many still exist, such as the magnificent Pont du Gard in Provence (begun by Agrippa in 19 BC). The *Cloaca maxima* (main drain) still forms part of the drainage system of modern Rome. Hippocrates, the "Father of

Medicine", recommended boiling water to filter out impurities, those particles that pollute its sweet taste, mar its clarity or poison the palate.

As the nineteenth century came to a close, chlorination was introduced and bacterial contamination became a thing of the past in advanced countries. It took just a few parts per million of this common element to render supplies completely free of bacteria and its strong taste could be largely removed by sodium sulphite treatment.

Who would have thought that a century later, as the result of the activities of a bunch of fanatical wiseacres, contaminated drinking water would once again result in the deaths of thousands of people from cholera? But more of that later.

Meanwhile, it is useful to examine the progress of the application of statistical inference, the power of which had been so dramatically demonstrated by Snow.

4. Legacy of the preacher of rigour

If your experiment needs statistics, you ought to have done a better experiment.
Ernest Rutherford

Sir Ronald Fisher, (1890-1962), was a British mathematician, whose life's work was to develop statistical theories to make scientific experimentation far more reliable. He made original contributions to the subject as early as 1912, while still an undergraduate at Cambridge. He applied his methods first in biology, but his statistical methodology quickly became influential and was applied in agricultural, medical and industrial research. It was therefore a remarkable and enduring irony that Fisher, the founder of rigorous objective statistical methods, should provide the means by which the science of epidemiology, among others, was undermined.

There seems to be an ironic rule of opposites when one looks at the historic results of the work of great men. In the name of gentle Jesus, meek and mild, more people would be tortured and massacred than in any other. Ivan the Terrible, who deliberately set out to make torture and massacre his life's work, is now worshipped as a saint in some parts of Russia. Fisher, whose mission was to bring rigour and probity into the use of statistical inference, in vital areas achieved precisely the opposite. The damage is caused not by the great men themselves, but by their lesser followers, who distort, dogmatise and abuse their teachings.

Fisher's contribution to the theory of statistical sampling was a remarkable one. Important results in the subject had been obtained by the likes of Helmert, Pearson and Student (W.S.Gossett), but Fisher was the first to conduct a systematic investigation. The methods he used were very advanced and would not be appropriate here. They included such techniques as analytical geometry in multidimensional space. He was able to produce rigorous proofs of results that had been known earlier and find new results in a number of fundamentally important cases.

In order to understand the magnitude of Fisher's task in bringing rigour to the scientific uses of statistics one has to take into account the nature of the problem and people's understanding of it. The heart of the problem is the concept of probability. It is so central that we need to make some points of clarification.

A diversion on probability

The basic problem is that probability theory is not easy. Some writers pretend otherwise, but there are many examples showing that even relative experts can get confused over a quite simple problem, as we shall see below. There is even a considerable difficulty in defining what probability is.

The classical definition

Until the twentieth century the whole theory of probability was based on the classical definition. In this we count the total number of possible outcomes, N, and the number of outcomes favourable to a particular event a, which we call N_a. the probability of event a is then given by:

$$P_a = \frac{N_a}{N}$$

Thus, if we wish to determine the probability of obtaining an even number on rolling a fair die, we count the number of even faces, divide it by the total number of faces and get the obvious result of one half. That all seems simple enough, but it is surprising how soon we can get into difficulties if we slightly complicate the experiment.

Let us say we wish to determine the probability of obtaining a total of seven on rolling two dice. We might say that the number of possible outcomes is the eleven possible sums, which give us the result:

$$P_7 = \tfrac{1}{11}$$

On the other hand we could count the total number of possible pairs of numbers, which is 21, and determine that only three are favourable to the event, namely (3,4), (5,2) and (1,6), which gives us a different result:

$$P_7 = \tfrac{3}{21} = \tfrac{1}{7}$$

A third approach is to distinguish between the two dice, so that (3,4) is treated as a different outcome from (4,3), which gives us yet another result:

$$P_7 = \tfrac{6}{36} = \tfrac{1}{6}$$

Thus we have three different estimates of probability for the same event. Most people after a little thought would say that the third is correct and the first two wrong, but why? We reason that the outcomes in the first two cases were not equally likely. Therefore we can only achieve a right answer if we count outcomes that are equally likely. However, *equally likely* means *equally probable*, which means that our definition is circular, in that we need the concept of probability to define probability.

We get into further difficulties if we complicate the situation even further. Suppose the dice are loaded, so that the probabilities of the faces are not equal. The definition is of no help to us at all.

The relative frequency definition

This is considered a more practical idea and therefore favoured by engineers and physicists. Suppose a trial is repeated N times and the event a occurs N_a times, then the ratio of N_a to N converges on a number as N gets bigger, and we call this number the probability. In mathematical notation:

$$P_a = \lim_{N \to \infty} \frac{N_a}{N}$$

The weakness of this version is obvious. We cannot perform an infinite number of experiments, or even a large number, or in some cases any at all.

The axiomatic definition

A more satisfying approach is the same one we use in other branches of mathematics, such as geometry. We simply have to accept that in order to build up a theory we have to take as an act of faith that certain concepts, such as a point or line, actually exist. We assume that there is a number, P_a, that can be assigned to an event a with the following properties:

1. P_a is positive
2. There exists a *certain* event for which the probability equals 1.
3. If two events are mutually exclusive the probability of either or both of them happening is the sum of their individual probabilities.

In fact we need only these three axioms to build up the whole of the theory of probability, just as we do with geometry. For a clear exposition of this see the book by Papoulis (bibliography), an engineer with a rigorous but perspicuous approach, from which the above illustrations are taken. The situation is, indeed, no different from that obtaining in geometry. When Euclid defines a point as "that which has no part" or a straight line as "the shortest distance between two points" he is adopting axioms, rather than something that can be attested to by the human senses. Once the axioms are accepted all the theorems of geometry, such as the one conventionally ascribed to Pythagoras, follow as a logical sequence.

Many mathematicians, including Fisher, reject the axiomatic approach because of an elaborate theorem, due to Gödel, which proved that such a system could not be proved to be free of contradictions. We might as well reject the whole of Euclid on the same grounds. The alternative seems to be some sort of mishmash in which the beliefs of various practitioners divide and subdivide into various theological sects.

Probability as a measure of belief

In the real world we often have to rely on our own reasoning; for example as to whether the accused is guilty of the crime. Inductive reasoning is often used in the development of scientific theories and the rigorous theorems of the textbooks come as an afterthought. There are clear dangers here. Our beliefs may well be founded on false observation, erroneous reasoning or sheer blind prejudice. We all of us, including scientists, rely on our intuition when assessing chance. Our intuition is not a reliable ally; it can often play us false, even in fairly simple experiments. There is one famous example that has appeared under various headings, such as Bertrand's box paradox. It reappeared more recently as the result of an argument about a television quiz game. See Ian Stewart's *The Magical Maze* (bibliography) for an entertaining account, which is condensed below.

The answer's a lemon

A contestant in a TV quiz is faced with three doors. Behind one is a brand new car and behind each of the others is the booby prize, say a lemon. The contestant chooses a door, but the host, who knows where the prize is, opens one of the two remaining doors and shows there is a lemon behind it. The contestant is then allowed to change his mind and go for the remaining door or stay with his original choice. Which should he do? Before reading on, think about it.

Almost everybody, including trained scientists, rely on their intuition and immediately say that swapping makes no difference, since there is an equal chance of the car being behind each of the remaining doors. This answer is **wrong** and the contestant can in fact double his chances by swapping. When this correct solution was aired on TV there was a furore, with denunciations from hundreds of scientists including research statisticians in senior positions. We can demonstrate the correct answer by making tables of the possible outcomes of the two strategies. For simplicity we will use C to represent the car and L the lemon. We label the contestant's first choice "Door 1". The ones that the contestant can then choose in the second round are in bold, as are the winning strategies in each case.

Door 1	Door 2	Door 3	Winning strategy
C	**L**	**L**	**Don't swap**
L	**C**	L	**Swap**
L	L	**C**	**Swap**

How can our intuition be so wrong? I was caught out myself until I thought about it. The answer is that we fail to allow for the prior knowledge of the host. He knows where the car is, and unless the contestant was right the first time (one chance in three), he is forced to uncover the only other wrong door, thus revealing the location of the car.

Thus the contestant's chances of winning if he does not swap doors are 1/3, but if he does swap they rise to 2/3. The doubling of one's chances is no trivial matter, yet the fact is not immediately apparent to most people. There are a number of simple and relevant observations we can make about this simple example.

1. It is an exercise in *conditional probability* as the host's behaviour is conditioned by the contestant's first random choice. Conditional probabilities are considerably more tricky to deal with than simple ones.
2. Intuition is a very poor guide in such problems. Sometimes we exercise our intuition without realising it, as the answer seems so obvious.

3. Prior knowledge has a powerful and mischievous effect, even in a simple example. Imagine how powerful and misleading it can be in a complicated field trial.
4. This simple exercise has appeared in various forms in elementary textbooks on probability for more than a century. Yet thousands of professional users of probability theory were fooled by it when it resurfaced. Apparently some of them became quite aggressive about it.

The predecessors

It was an obscure English clergyman, Thomas Bayes, who made the first serious attempt to bring rationality into the process of scientific inference in the real world of random events. He was a notable mathematician, with many publications in *Philosophical Transactions*. Significantly, he did not publish his postulate, which produced what has become known as *Bayes' Theorem*, during his lifetime, possibly because he had doubts about its validity. It was communicated to the Royal Society by his friend Richard Price in 1763, two years after Bayes' death. It is another enduring irony of the history of statistics that Bayes, the first in the field, should return to haunt his successors by being the centre of a dispute about the very foundations of the subject. Without going into inappropriate detail, we may remark that the crucial aspect of Bayes' theorem is the provision to insert a prior estimate of probability, and it is the status and validity of such *a priori* probabilities that is the crux of the argument.

The great mathematician Laplace (1749-1827) established much of the theory of probability, as did Pascal, Fermat, Leibnitz, Montmort, Bernoulli and De Moivre. There is little scope to question the validity of this vast mathematical structure, but there remains a great amount of disputation about what we mean by the word *probability*. It is very much like theological disputation in which all arguments can be traced back to a fundamental unanswerable question, such as "Who created God?" The steps in a theological argument might be immaculately logical, but the problems reside in both the starting assumptions and the use that is made of the conclusions.

Perhaps a better analogy would be of a beautifully designed girder bridge, each member carefully calculated to bear its precisely assigned compression or tension, a thing of architectural beauty because the engineering is right. On the banks of the river, however, the ends of the bridge are resting on mounds of sand. For, while the purity and correctness of mathematical statistics are indisputable, what is done with the inputs and outputs is very often highly questionable.

For some decades the statistician carried out the functions that are now assigned to the computer. The client presented the data, perhaps having sought advice on the design of the experiment, and then received the analysis. The statistician used tables created by the likes of Fisher to calculate whether the outcome was significant to the predetermined level. While, again, the internal mathematical basis was quite rigorous, there was a possibility for wide variation, not least in the choice

of statistical procedures. The statistician, nevertheless, exercised a moderating influence on procedures, assumptions and claims, which is now largely absent.

One of the mounds of sand is the definition of probability itself – what we might call the theology of statistics. When statisticians gather they agree on the mathematics but they argue about the meaning of probability (see, for example, Savage et al, bibliography). The other mound of sand is in the applications to which the theory is put.

Significance testing

The great contribution that Fisher made was in the statistical testing of scientific hypotheses. It was far from being his only contribution, though to read much of the scientific literature you might think so.

The problem of significance testing is perhaps best explained by taking a simple example. Suppose you were a casino inspector and you suspect that a die in use is loaded to produce an excess number of sixes. How would you test it? An obvious answer is that you roll the die a large number of times and check whether the relative frequency is what you would theoretically expect, which is, of course, 1/6 or approximately 0.167. This apparently simple idea introduces a number of problems. What do we mean by a large number? Is it 10, 100, 1000 or more? In practice the relative frequency is never exactly 1/6. In fact with the numbers of rolls just suggested it cannot be, since the result must be a whole number but 1/6 produces a recurring decimal. For 100 rolls the mathematical expectation for the number of sixes would be 16.6666 and the expected relative frequency still 0.167.

The first important remark to make is that your inspection task is literally a mission impossible. There is a finite probability that the relative frequency in any particular series of tests can take on any value between zero and one. Obviously the probability of one of these extremes happening becomes vanishingly small as you increase the number of throws, but it is never exactly zero. If you restrict yourself to ten throws of a fair die, there is a probability of 0.161 that you will get no sixes at all. For a hundred throws, however, this reduces to one in a hundred million. It is an interesting sidelight to the gambling instinct that the chances of winning the British National Lottery are equivalent to getting no sixes in ninety throws of the die. Figure 4.1 shows the distribution of probabilities of the relative frequencies for (a) 10, (b)100 and (c)1000 throws.

We can see that the scatter (the "width") of the distribution decreases as the number of throws, N, increases. It does this, however, in proportion to the square root of N, so we get a law of diminishing returns and have to quadruple the number of throws to halve the scatter. This introduces a practical issue, the time taken to perform the test. Anything over about 100 throws would be unconscionably time-consuming.

Let us suppose that the die is in fact biased to produce a 50% excess of sixes, so that the chance of success is one in four. This could be highly profitable for anyone skilled in palming the dice, without being obvious to the onlooker. The comparison of the loaded die with the fair die is shown in Figure 4.1 (d), which represents the distributions for 100 throws. Clearly if our test produces 30 sixes out of our 100 throws we could be reasonably satisfied that we have a loaded die. There is the same chance, however, that we would get 20 sixes, for which the probabilities are the same for the loaded and fair dice.

This encapsulates the problem of significance testing. In this case, any reasonable person would accept that 30 out of 100 sixes would establish significant evidence that we have a loaded die, and equally that 20 would not produce significant evidence. What happens, however, if our result is somewhere between these two numbers?

The procedure adopted is based on our wish to test our hypothesis that the die is loaded. In order to do this, we test the *null* hypothesis (usually referred to as H_0) that the die is not loaded. In statistical parlance, H_0 is that our sample number is from the population of fair die as shown in Figure 4.1(b). The possible amount of loading is unknown, so all we have to work on is the statistical properties of a fair die. It is fairly straightforward to calculate from the formula for a binomial distribution the probability of getting n or more successes in 100 throws for a probability of 1/6, and we can tabulate them for the relevant range:

n	Prob %
20	15.4
21	10.2
22	6.4
23	3.9
24	2.2
25	1.2
26	0.6
27	0.3
28	0.2
29	0.1

Now we come to the crucial problem – where to draw the line? We have to make the decision that one of these numbers is insignificant and the next one down is significant, which means choosing a significance level as a percentage of probability. In practice, of course, you only make one trial and produce one result. Let us assume that you make your inspection and assume beforehand that you will set a limit of 5%. Your null hypothesis is that the parameter of the distribution is one sixth, whereas the alternative hypothesis is that it is greater than this. Assume further that on performing the test you get 23 sixes out of your 100 throws. Your experiment then "proves" that the die is loaded and you send the croupier to prison, since the probability of getting this number or greater is 3.9%. Are you happy to do this? Furthermore, if you make 100 inspections during the course of a year you are likely to send five innocent croupiers to prison. Have you carried out your duties in a fair and just way? What if a new draconian law made using a loaded die a capital offence? Would this change your attitude?

In the above we have asserted that the probability of throwing a six with a fair die is precisely 1/6, neither more nor less. Whether we do this as a measure of belief or simply take it as the axiomatic definition of fairness is neither here nor there. It would be deemed very eccentric to propose any other value, but this is a very simple case. What if we are discussing the chances of ourselves as individuals contracting a particular form of cancer during our lives?

Most reasonable people would by this stage be rather dubious about the choice of 5% as the limit of acceptance. Yet that is precisely the limit that is applied in a wide range of studies. In at least one notorious case, as we shall see, when the study did not produce the "desired" result, the researchers increased the limit to 10%, a one in ten chance of being wrong. Changing horses in mid-stream in this way is rightly regarded as a scientific crime. The consequences of the application of the 5% limit in terms of health, economy and society have been vast and incalculable.

It is not simply the matter of the choice of limit that is a cause of concern. It is now accepted by a large number of statisticians that the whole concept of significance testing has been grossly over-emphasised. It has become a quasi-religious rite, with untutored participants practising cookbook techniques that they do not understand. The aptness of the religious analogy is marked, as we shall see below.

It can be (and often has been) argued that Fisher and his like have created a monster in the testing of the significance of hypotheses. There are hundreds of quotations from eminent scientists and statisticians to this effect (see for example the collections by Nester and Parkhurst available on the Web). As is happening more and more frequently in human affairs, the means is becoming the end. Mediocre researchers regard the value of P as the product of their efforts, rather than a tool to establish scientific truths. Here are just a few quotations from eminent authors taken from the collections mentioned:

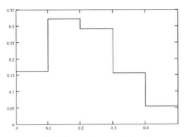

(a) Probablity against relative frequency for 10 throws

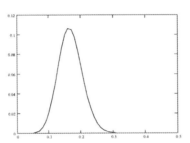

(b) Probability against relative frequency for 100 throws

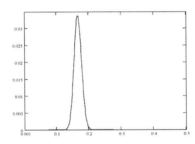

(c) Probability against relative frequency for 1000 throws

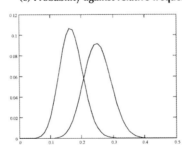

(d) Fair die and loaded die for 100 throws

Figure 4.1 Relative Frequencies of throwing a six

The emphasis given to formal tests of signiThe emphasis given to formal test of sigmificance throughout [R.A. Fisher's] Statistical Methods...has caused scientific research workers to pay undue attention to the results of the tests of significance they perform on their data, particularly data derived from experiments, and too little to the estimates of the magnitude of the effects they are investigating. ... The emphasis on tests of significance and the consideration of the results of each experiment in isolation, have had the unfortunate consequence that scientific workers have often regarded the execution of a test of significance on an experiment as the ultimate objective." (Yates 1951)

The most commonly occurring weakness in the application of Fisherian methods is undue emphasis on tests of significance, and failure to recognize that in many types of experimental work estimates of the treatment effects, together with estimates of the errors to which they are subject, are the quantities of primary interest. (Yates 1964)

When a Fisherian null hypothesis is rejected with an associated probability of, for example, .026, it is not the case that the probability that the null hypothesis is true is .026 (or less than .05, or any other value we can specify). Given our framework of probability as long-run relative frequency (as much as we might wish it to be otherwise) this result does not tell us about the truth of the null hypothesis, given the data. (For this we have to go to Bayesian or likelihood statistics, in which probability is not relative frequency but degree of belief.)" (Cohen 1990)

Of course, everyone knows that failure to reject the Fisherian null hypothesis does not warrant the conclusion that it is true. Fisher certainly knew and emphasized it, and our textbooks duly so instruct us. Yet how often do we read in the discussion and conclusions of articles now appearing in our most prestigious journals that 'there is no difference' or 'no relationship'? (Cohen 1990)

If the null hypothesis is not rejected, Fisher's position was that nothing could be concluded. But researchers find it hard to go to all the trouble of conducting a study only to conclude that nothing can be concluded. (Schmidt 1996)

Randomisation

Fisher's book on experimental design rapidly became the bible for experimenters using statistical methods. As with the Holy Bible, however, followers of the creed were somewhat selective in the bits that they used and those they ignored. In particular, Fisher, right from the start of the book, lays great emphasis on the importance of randomisation if significance testing is to be used. Fisher gives two examples that underline the essential requirement for randomisation, the first a little frivolous and the second at the core of his agricultural studies.

Fisher conjectures that a certain lady claims to be able to distinguish between tea in which the milk has been added first and that where it has been added second. How do we test this? If we pour four cups onto milk and then four cups into which milk is added, there is more than one difference between the two groups of four. The second group will have been in the pot longer and will therefore be more concentrated and cooler when it is mixed. Any difference detected by the claimant could be caused by one of these factors and not the order of mixing. It is therefore necessary to randomise the order in which the samples are prepared.

Fisher's second example reminds us that his chair at Cambridge was in Genetics. One of his great preoccupations was comparing varieties of crops and their treatment. Suppose the requirement is to determine the most effective of three fertilisers on a particular vegetable crop. One could divide the plot into three equal contiguous blocks and apply the fertilisers to them. The haunting question then is "What if there is an unidentified vein of rich soil running through the plot?" The result of the experiment would be totally invalid, but in a way that is invisible to the experimenter. It is for this reason that Fisher devoted much thought to the layout of randomised plots, in the form of Latin squares or even Græco-Latin and higher squares, which were designed to remove any accidental correlation with soil variations.

Let it not be thought that Fisher in any way regarded randomisation as an optional extra to significance testing. One of the earliest sub-headings in his seminal book is **Randomisation; the Physical Basis of the validity of the Test**. Fisher's many words on the subject can be boiled down to a simple statement – **no randomisation means no significance!**

The requirement for randomisation poses a fundamental problem for studies into human beings. There are profound ethical considerations. To test the effects of smoking on health, for example, the strictly Fisherian approach would be to select two groups of say a thousand teenagers by lot, then detail one group to smoke for the rest of their lives and the other group to refrain. It is inconceivable that anyone could propose such a procedure in a just society.

Thus experimenters are reduced to performing "observational studies" on people as they are, without randomisation. They then apply Fisherian methods to obtain a measure of significance, despite the great man himself having precluded any such calculation. Thus we get, time and time again, the magical formula that graces the front of this book – $P<0.05$, of which more, much, much more later.

Civil war

The utterly memorable struggle between the Cavaliers (Wrong but Wromantic) and the Roundheads (Right but Repulsive).
1066 and all that – Sellar and Yeatman

The Cavaliers represent the original ruling class, deriving their provenance from the original work of Bayes. They are known by various titles, such as Bayesians or subjectivists. Their basic tenet of belief is that the prior plausibility of an experimental result must be taken into account, which is done by application of Bayes' theorem. The objectivists or frequentists are the Roundheads, guardians of the puritan faith, with Fisher cast in the role of Lord Protector. They recoil at the thought of subjectivity entering scientific argument. Now it is natural for scientists to lean towards the objectivist approach, since they persuade themselves that all science is objective, a moot point. Thus it is probably true that a majority of practising scientists lean in this direction. Following the recognition of the particle/wave duality it is now a familiar concept that two apparently contradictory explanations can be correct (or, indeed, incorrect). We are faced, however, with a substantial and unresolved dilemma.

The inherent problems of such a theological argument can often be exposed by taking an extreme case. Suppose, for example, we form the hypothesis that wearing red trousers causes heart disease. We might get a result from an investigation that attests to the truth of this hypothesis at the five-percent level. The Roundheads would argue that we have to take this result at face value, since all hypotheses are equal in their sight, while the Cavaliers would say that we have to take into account the self-evident absurdity of the proposition and insert a low prior probability into a Bayesian calculation. Our result might be purely fortuitous; we have won the one-in-twenty lottery. On the other hand, the wearing of red trousers might be associated with a particular cultural group who share common dietary habits, which would be a *confounding factor*.

The differences in results obtained if prior plausibility is taken into account by means of Bayes' Theorem are profound. In the following table due to Matthews, we see the chances of data being nothing more than a fluke for various initial levels of plausibility.

Initial level of plausibility (prior chances of effect being real)	Chances of data significant at P=0.05 being a fluke
1 in 2	0.22
1 in 10	0.71
1 in 100	0.96
1 in 1000	1.000

Thus, even if we take the agnostic view that the effect is just as likely to be real as it is to be false, the magic 5% becomes an impotent 22%. This all begs the question "How do we choose the prior level of plausibility?" You might well decide that our red trouser hypothesis is so unlikely that we put it at the 1 in 1000 level, which would mean that no experiment could possibly provide a positive result. A reasonable conclusion perhaps, but substitute for red trousers some other objects of conjecture that occur in the literature and you have a profound problem. Putative causes of heart disease have included a bacterium that only resides in the digestive system and passive smoking, which produces concentrations of nicotine lower than those produced by the natural diet. Most detached observers would regard both these hypotheses as fundamentally implausible, but those who adhere to them would take the other view.

Where did he go wrong?

As observed at the beginning of this chapter, the legacies of great men are often nothing of their doing. Fisher is largely credited with sanctioning the talismanic P<0.05 for all experimental circumstances. He no more did this than Jesus sanctioned the selling of indulgences by the pardoners of Chaucer's time. To Fisher, as a mathematician, P was merely a disposable parameter, one that could be set at any value that was appropriate to the circumstances. Late in his life he remarked that the value of 0.05 was simply a mathematical convenience. But, as in Monty Python's *The Life of Brian*, a chance remark of the chosen prophet is translated into a fundamental tenet of belief by the faithful followers. Just as modern permissive Anglican bishops quietly drop the inconvenient parts of the Holy Bible, so many experimenters dispose of the strict requirements of the Fisherian method.

The contrast between the elegance of Fisher's mathematical structure and the crudity of its application is a striking one. It is like a hunter commissioning the manufacture of a fine shooting piece, engineered with precision and inlaid with precious metals, and then taking it out in the field to use it as a bludgeon to club his prey to death.

Nevertheless, even allowing for the distortions to which Fisher's methods have been subjected over the years, there remain serious questions about the whole ethos. The conflicting arguments mounted by the Bayesians and the Frequentists are far too abstruse to be rehearsed here. They are nicely summarised by Robert Matthews in his ESEF pamphlet *Statistical snake-oil* and in his web articles. The proof of the pudding is in the eating. So-called objective methods repeatedly come up with absurd results. Great drug breakthroughs dissolve away in the light of experience. Many putative causes of disease are so implausible that they are laughable (though this does not prevent them from being extensively touted, especially if they are politically correct or industrially profitable). There is little doubt that conventional significance testing greatly exaggerates the merit of spurious results.

The inherent problems of statistical sampling are glaringly obvious to any layman who follows the results of political opinion polls. The mathematical theory on which they are based, thanks to people like Fisher, is exact; yet the results of almost simultaneous polls can vary widely and they are often proved totally wrong by the subsequent real election (1992 in the UK, for example).

Opinion polls, which made the fortunes of the likes of George Gallup, reveal many of the problems of statistical sampling that are independent of the rigorous mathematical structure on which they are based. The primary problem is that they involve people, who do not always tell the truth, even to themselves. We have a marked tendency towards self-deception about things for which we have been induced to feel guilty; such as consumption of food and drink or voting out of self rather than the general interest. For this reason real science is rightly suspicious about surveys that are based on self-reporting, which an unfortunately large proportion are. Another problem is that subtle differences in the selection techniques can affect the results, as is demonstrated by consistent trends for particular polls to favour different parties in election campaigns. Third is the well-known phenomenon that the very act of measurement affects the result. The fact that a question is posed at all has an effect on people's thinking, while the framing and sequence of questions can predetermine the average person's response. This was brilliantly and comically illustrated in a *Yes Prime Minister* script, in which Sir Humphrey Appleby persuaded his colleague to vote "yes" then "no" to the same question by placing it at the end of two different sequences of tendentious questions. Some countries ban the publishing of opinion polls before elections because they can influence the results.

The whole mathematical theory of statistics and sampling is built up from remarkably few axioms. In itself it is exact and rigorous. In application however, it can be subjected to the effects of further covert axioms (such as the assumption that people tell the truth) and all the rigour collapses. Quite apart from the human influences, however, there are inherent problems with the statistics themselves. The results of a statistical calculation are always such that any decision made on its basis has a finite probability of being wrong. Fisher's great contribution was to quantify this wrongness in many important cases by assigning it a probability.

One of the factors that Fisher did not allow for was the sheer numbers of scientists who would be repeating the same trials. In his time science was independent of politics and political correctness. Scientists were still relatively few in number and it would be a remarkable coincidence if even two were performing the same tests. There were no "publish of perish" pressures, while the patronage of science was diffuse and undirected. Universities were ivory towers without public relations departments, while the new popular media, with their addiction to scares, had yet to be born.

This gross miscalculation made by Fisher was one for which he could be entirely excused. Not only did he work in a world where scientists were still relatively few in number, those there were practised in a largely self-regulating environment, independently of powerful external patrons. It would have been inconceivable to him that one day dozens, even hundreds, of researchers would be working on similar projects. What seemed to him a small chance that an incorrect result could be published would within decades become a virtual certainty.

It is clear that, towards the end of his life, Fisher became rather concerned about the uses to which his methods were being bent. This is evinced by a sequence of letters he wrote to the *BMJ* and *Nature* on the smoking and lung cancer controversy. He was particularly incensed by the demand that "these hazards must be brought home to the public by all the modern devices of publicity". He pointed out that, if the original data of Sir Austin Bradford Hill showed that smoking causes lung cancer, they also showed that inhaling the smoke provides a cure. Furthermore, the observation that inhalers get fewer lung cancers was significant at the 1% level. Fisher was not the most perspicuous of writers (his treatment of Bayes' theorem is a monument of obscurity) and his stance on the smoking debate might be considered somewhat less than detached.

Had the realisation dawned on him that, like some latter day Frankenstein, he had taken part in the creation of a monster? It was one thing to use statistics to determine the likelihood that a particular gene had been inherited in a properly controlled and randomised laboratory experiment in cross-pollination, but quite another to use them to arouse alarm and despondency from uncontrolled observations on the population at large. In one case the penalty for being wrong might be a temporary diversion from the path to truth. In the other the penalty could be major disruption in the lives of millions of people. Thus a 5% level of significance in one context might be deemed to represent an acceptable risk of error, but in another it would be entirely unacceptable. Fisher had developed his methods in one context, only to find them indiscriminately applied in the other. Anyone who could look into the future would have said to him "Sir Ronald, you ain't seen nothing yet". He would have been truly horrified at what was to come.

What Fisher would not live to know was that he was witnessing the beginnings of a massive social change. It would encompass, among other phenomena, the Nanny State, Political Correctness and a wide scale proliferation of junk science. In the decade after his death, the Social Theory would be launched and almost everything he stood for set aside. The ultimate irony was that a key ingredient to this stew was the fact that he himself had been deemed to grant his imprimatur to the indiscriminate use of significance tests and, in particular, the 5% level of acceptance. In the early days, scientists would consult a professional statistician about the significance of their results, and he could often exercise a moderating influence. Now they simply plug their numbers into a statistical software package and that influence is gone.

When you have read what follows in this book you might well be inclined to say to Sir Ronald, in the words of the immortal Ollie "Here's another fine mess you've gotten us into."

In contrast to the mathematical rigour promoted by the likes of Fisher, there was an alternative approach, more sociological in nature; which brings us to our next topic.

5. Launch of the Social Theory

There is no nonsense so errant that it cannot be made the creed of the vast majority by adequate governmental action.
Bertrand Russell

Thomas McKeown was something of a renegade in the medical profession. He went to a London hospital as a medical student after several years of graduate research in biochemistry at McGill and human anatomy at Oxford. He formed a rather cynical view of the attitude of the staff. He noticed the absence of any real interest among the clinical teachers in the origin of disease or in whether the prescribed treatments were of any benefit to the patients. The first of these concerns was somewhat disingenuous, as he had not entered a department of epidemiology. The second might have been true in a particular department but, although interests are wider in an academic department where teaching and research run alongside treatment, it would not appear to be the norm. Nevertheless, he made it his life's work to challenge the claims of the medical profession to have revolutionised the well-being of mankind.

McKeown's writings made sufficient impact to change the world. Two books in particular were remarkably influential: *The Role of Medicine* and *The Origins of Human Disease*. The first of these in 1979 put a spanner in the works of scientific medicine, from which it was never to recover. The second in 1988 defined the New Epidemiology and, indeed, became its manifesto.

If you create a university chair in some new subject, it follows as the night the day that the occupant of that chair will see it as his duty to ensure that the subject is promoted as the most important thing in human existence. Thus a professor of, say, plastic doilies will seek to convince the world that such objects are the ultimate goal and achievement of human existence. McKeown became by a series of accidents Professor of Social Medicine. It was a title in tune with its time. The University had, in fact, wanted to create a department of occupational health, but the funding trust offered to support a chair in Social Medicine, which on the principle of not looking a gift horse in the mouth was accepted; an early step on the road to loss of independence by the universities. "Social" was the in word in post-war Britain. The study of kings and queens had been largely replaced by the study of the masses, Social History, while the so-called Social Sciences were beginning to gather momentum.

McKeown's timing was immaculate. His message was greeted with alacrity across the political spectrum. The left was delighted by the social content of the theory, while the right was given a reason to bear down on the growing costs of medical care. For the burden of the first of his two broadsides, though politely phrased, was little more than a savage attack on the ethos of modern medicine and a denigration of its achievements. He went on to contend that there were two major branches of disease – *diseases of poverty* and *diseases of affluence*, which were respectively largely infectious and non-infectious diseases.

Tuberculosis

McKeown's thesis is exemplified by his first major example, which is summarised in a graph of the death rates for tuberculosis over time from the mid-nineteenth to the mid-twentieth centuries. As can be seen from his graph in the figure, there is a steady decline throughout this period. In particular there are no marked discontinuities at what might be regarded as critical breakthroughs in scientific medicine; namely, discovery of the tubercle bacillus, the introduction of chemotherapy and the commencement of BCG vaccination.

The three events isolated by McKeown are important, but they are only part of a continuum of developments in the treatment of the disease by scientific medicine. In order to appreciate this fact it is necessary to examine the history of the illness and humanity's battle against it.

TB has been known throughout recorded history: The ancient Greeks called it *phthisis* (to waste). The swollen glands of the neck were called scrofula. In medieval times it was known as *The Kings Evil,* because newly crowned kings of

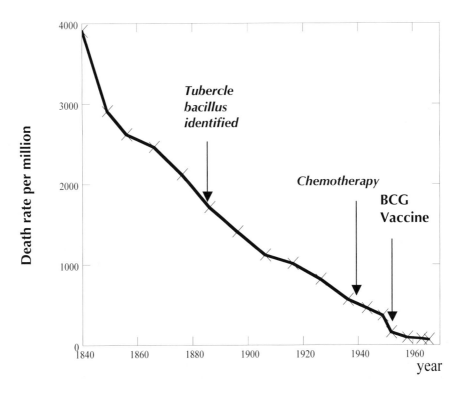

Figure 5.1 respiratory tuberculosis: mean annual death-rates (standardised to 1901 population): England and Wales (after McKeown).

England and France were believed to have powers to heal TB with their touch. This disease is, in fact, not particularly contagious. The tuberculosis bacterium spreads in droplets dispersed through the air by coughing, and the risk of catching it rises only when there is close and prolonged contact with a sufferer. Most of those who do become infected do not acquire the active form of disease. In fact, millions of westerners are infected with the tuberculosis organism but have no sign of disease; their immune systems control the latent infection and they do not spread the bacillus to others. They have about a 10% lifetime chance of developing the active form, usually in the first two years after acquiring the latent form of the disease.

The disease known as tuberculosis (TB) is caused by Mycobacterium tuberculosis, M. bovis, M. africanum, and M. microti. M. tuberculosis is usually pathogenic for humans, while M. bovis is usually pathogenic for animals. These bacteria belong to the family of Actinomycetales, which are non-motile and rod-like. Most Mycobacteria are benign, inhabiting water and soil and able to degrade various undesirable organic compounds. The above group, however, have become intracellular pathogens of higher vertebrates, inflicting great suffering and death in animals and humans. They are relatively slow growing with a generation time of 12 hours or more. Although TB is predominantly a disease of the lungs, about 15% of cases are non-pulmonary.

At the first point in McKeown's graph, tuberculosis was the major killer, dwarfing both cholera and typhus. About one in five of all people would experience it in their lifetime. It was accepted as a fact of life, even having a certain cachet, being associated with the artistic life, creative but short. It saw off the Bronte family, Chopin, Keats, Robert Louis Stevenson and the founder of Harvard University. In fiction and opera it disposed of the likes of Violetta and Mimi. In the early nineteenth century it might have accounted for one-third of all deaths. Alexander Dumas noted that it was the fashion to suffer from the lungs; everybody was consumptive, poets especially. It was good form to spit blood and to die before reaching the age of thirty. Eugene O'Neill recorded his disillusion on discovering that the social cachet of TB was misplaced. One day a friend, an eminent TB specialist, told him the truth – that autopsies revealed the democratic fact that nearly everyone has had it.

As McKeown's graph clearly demonstrates, in little over a century TB had been reduced from humanity's greatest threat to a minor hazard. What is less clearly established is his contention that this had little or nothing to do with the activities of scientific medicine.

The flaws in the reasoning

The great lacuna in McKeown's evidence was his complete disregard of the response of scientific medicine to the recognition that TB was a contagion. It was as far back as 1720 that Benjamin Marten first conjectured in *A New Theory of Consumption* that TB could be caused by "wonderfully minute living creatures". In 1796, Edward Jenner had performed the first immunisation and in 1849 John

Snow's cholera pamphlet was published. These were just a few of the major advances, but more significant was the accumulation of minor advances, many of which went unrecorded. As real understanding of the nature of infectious disease began to percolate through the profession, so medical practice improved by thousands of small steps. The sanatorium system began in Europe in the 1850s, but clearly awareness of the benefits of isolation must have preceded this, and it is almost certain that the first point on the graph approximately marks the beginning of this form of medical intervention. Thus, far from undermining the status of scientific medicine, the graph is a dramatic testament to its value.

By the time that the great success of chemotherapy was achieved in TB, the disease had been largely conquered by existing intervention. Nevertheless, it was still a fatal disease. On November 20, 1944, antibiotic was administered for the first time to a critically ill TB patient, with immediate and impressive effect. His advanced disease was visibly arrested, the bacteria disappeared from his sputum, and he made a rapid recovery. This marked the beginning of the end of the sanatorium movement, one of the greatest successes of scientific medicine.

The most damning evidence against the McKeown doctrine was to emerge later. His contention that the disease was decreasing to zero, irrespective of the efforts of doctors, was blown out of the water when incidence of tuberculosis began to increase. The last point of his graph was not a zero; it was a minimum. In England and Wales, for example, notifications of tuberculosis increased by 12% between 1988 and 1992. TB deaths in the UK were 106 per million in 1995, 107 in 1996 and 108 in 1997. By 2004 there were 7,000 cases in the UK, a rise of 1,000 in a decade.

According to the WHO, tuberculosis is now the world's deadliest disease. It would be easy, of course, to oversimplify and fall into McKeown's own trap. A number of factors were operating, including an expansion of world travel and large-scale migration. More ominous was the appearance of antibiotic-resistant forms of the bacterium. According to the social theory, this should have been an irrelevance.

Of course, tuberculosis was only the first of many of McKeown's examples, but they all follow the same pattern. Pneumonia, diphtheria, smallpox, poliomyelitis, whooping cough and measles all showed the same falling trend. However, McKeown's account of the decline in mortality for these various important diseases is so selective that it may be considered quite perverse. In particular, he completely ignores the fact that the early nineteenth century marks the beginning of the era of scientific medicine. Of course, the way had been paved by various geniuses of the previous three centuries. Vesalius (1514-1564) pioneered anatomy at Padua. William Harvey (1578-1657) discovered the circulation of the blood. Thomas Sydenham (1624-1689) made the first systematic classification of disease. The Dutch draper, Antonie Van Leeuwenhoek, first observed micro-organisms in 1680. The stethoscope was invented by René Théophile Hyacinthe Laënnec (1781-1826).

By 1800 medicine was becoming scientific and, in particular, so was medical education.

When Beeton's Christmas Annual in 1887 published a story called *A study in scarlet*, the popular detective was born. Arthur Conan Doyle, however, had based the character of Sherlock Holmes on the professor who had taught him at the University of Edinburgh, one Dr Joseph Bell, who had in fact written the preface to the story. Bell had developed the art of diagnosis into a scientific consideration of the available evidence. In his words "The precise and intelligent recognition and appreciation of minor differences is the real essential factor in all successful medical diagnosis."

Ignoring the progress of medical practice is not the only fault in the reasoning. There are major and well-known fallacies throughout the argument. First and foremost, McKeown makes the cardinal error of confusing a statistical association with causality. It is indisputable that infectious diseases are statistically associated with poverty, while non-infectious diseases are associated with wealth. Poverty is also associated with malnutrition, ignorance of disease, lack of hygiene, restricted access to medical care, proliferation of vermin etc. Would a simple injection of money obviate all these adverse circumstances? Cultural and educational deprivation is as much the cause of poverty as its consequence. The poor are trapped in a cycle of such unfortunate associations. The biggest trap that McKeown falls into, however, is the independence fallacy. Everybody has to die of something. As you remove more and more of the major causes of premature death, such as infectious diseases, it follows inevitably that the remaining causes must become more and more prominent. Thus, though as always in such discussions there is a grain of truth, the occurrence of the observed rise of the so-called diseases of affluence requires nothing more than the removal of other forms of disease.

McKeown paints a rather idyllic view of the life of primitive man, in which the only serious hazard to a long life was hunger. This plays down a number of beneficial features of modern life. Take surgery, for example. I have reached an unnatural old age, not only because modern medicine has cured me of a number of potentially fatal diseases, but also because in my youth I had two quite serious limb fractures surgically reduced. I would not have survived long in the primitive world agonisingly maimed. Furthermore, it is unlikely that man experienced real hunger until he started to push out from his original sub-tropical paradise into more hostile territory.

Are we really supposed to accept that infectious disease barely existed in the primitive world; that not only the parasites but also our elaborate immune system suddenly sprang into being when man started artificially to congregate in agricultural communities? Unquestionably crowding aids the transmission of infection, but it is not the sole requirement. Tribes were not entirely isolated: they fought, killed and ate each other. The evolutionary advantage that led to the development of man's great brain was more likely to be found in battle tactics than food gathering. The development of a peaceful, indolent lifestyle is confined to a few isolated benign locations. To take an avian analogy, the bowerbird can afford to spend its time in elaborate architectural courtship rituals because food is plentiful. If it had to eke out its existence on the Antarctic ice its priorities would change.

Consequences of the theory

Without doubt, this was one of the most profoundly influential philosophical developments in human history. It brought about a revolution in social behaviour, ushering in such developments as the Nanny State and environmental quangos.

The worst consequence of the overwhelming popularity of the social theory was the complacency it induced. There was a serious penalty to pay and it was paid by the millions who died as a result of the retreat from scientifically established forms of intervention, such as insecticides and chlorination.

Graduates turned away from medical research and towards expertise in diagnostic instrumentation. Massive resources were poured into such developments as tomographic scanners; with, it has to be said, great benefits.

The new epidemiology, seriously flawed by being based on weak statistical associations, burgeoned in the universities and government funded institutions and was favoured with a massive provision of resources at the expense of real scientific and medical research.

Politicians, bureaucrats and self-appointed experts arrogated to themselves the right to harangue the general population on its lifestyle and used regulation and taxation to enforce conformity. Dieticians became the new *Gauleiters*, issuing diktats based on the most tenuous of evidence. McKeown was not just an innocent initiator of all of this. He concludes his discussion of *Evidence Required for Public Action* with the remark "… it should be recognised that conclusive evidence of harm or benefit is often an unrealistic requirement." Read in the light of some of the dubious research reviewed elsewhere in this book, this is rather sinister comment. He clearly favoured regimentation of the population for its own good. He was disingenuous in citing the cases of the Broad Street pump and thalidomide to justify forceful intervention. There is a world of difference between someone, in full possession of the information on the dangers, lighting a cigarette or abstaining from exercise and someone being exposed to peril by a hidden hazard in drinking water or a prescribed drug. In many cases, there is also a world of difference in the quality of the evidence. Like Torquemada or Cromwell he saw it as his duty to save others from themselves.

Books on health, with little or no reference to scientific medicine, became one of the largest branches of published literature. The more bizarre effusions of the new epidemiologists became accepted facts. McKeown was not just the father of the new epidemiology. He was the founder of a whole new social system.

Clearly, at the root of the problems raised by McKeown, is the question of cause and effect. This is not as easy a topic as is often glibly assumed, but it is necessary to make some effort to investigate the implications of the dilemmas that it introduces.

6. Cause and Effect

Another thing I must point out is that you cannot prove a vague theory wrong. ... Also, if the process of computing the consequences is indefinite, then with a little skill any experimental results can be made to look like the expected consequences.
Richard Feynman

Even from the superficial treatment in the introduction, it is quite clear that the key problem of epidemiology is the one of cause and effect. What do we mean when we say B is caused by A? For example, it is almost universally accepted that heart attacks are caused by eating butter. How confident can we be that this statement is true?

Following John Snow's work on the Broad Street pump it could confidently be claimed that drinking water contaminated with human faeces causes cholera, but would it be true? We can now assert that drinking severely contaminated water in which the cholera germ is absent does not cause cholera. On the other hand drinking distilled water to which the cholera germ has been added would cause cholera. The reason that we can make these statements with confidence is that the actual causative agent of cholera, which is the bacterium *Vibrio cholerae*, was discovered in 1883 by the German doctor and bacteriologist Robert Koch. Because of this knowledge we can confidently make two statements:

1. Cholera will occur only if the bacterium is present.
2. Cholera will never occur if the bacterium is absent.

In the thirty years interval between the work of Snow and that of Koch this knowledge was not available. The statement that drinking contaminated water causes cholera was to all intents and purposes a true one. It was certainly useful as a working hypothesis and, equally importantly, as a propaganda tool to persuade the population to mend its ways. It carried the additional benefit of preventing other diseases, but that was not appreciated at the time.

The situation is the same today with regard to smoking and lung cancer. The mandatory statement on the cigarette packet tells us that "Smoking causes lung cancer" but is it true? Thanks to the work of Hill and Doll we know that cigarette smoking is associated with an increase of about twenty times in the probability of contracting lung cancer (in the UK), but we do not know the causative agent for lung cancer, if indeed any exists. In the absence of other knowledge we have to allow for the possibility that lung cancer is a random event, like the radioactive decay of a radium atom. Behaviour might change the probability of that event occurring, but in does not become the cause. If you sleep outside the cave you are more likely to be struck by lightning than if you sleep inside, but the relocation of your bedding does not cause the lightning.

We might conclude that the two numbered statements above constitute the best and most rigorous definition of cause and effect, but unfortunately it is still not as simple as that. If we allow that some of the population will have developed resistance to cholera, though the statements remain true we can admit a modification:

1. Cholera will sometimes occur if the bacterium is present.
2. Cholera will never occur if the bacterium is absent.

We then arrive at the concept of **falsifiability**, as elaborated by Karl Popper. The only truly scientific test of the causal relationship between the bacterium and the disease is represented by the second statement. Just one case of cholera without the bacterium being present would rule out the theory that it is the cause. One case with the bacterium present would not have the same authority; after all there are thousands of species of bacteria present in the human body. Some of them can remain there with no effect for years before suddenly initiating disease, meningitis being a dramatic case in point.

Unfortunately, the problem is still more complicated, since one effect may be attributed to more than one cause. Suppose we replace "cholera" in the above argument by something more general, say "vomiting". While the bacterium, through a chain of events can be the primal cause of vomiting, so can many other things, over-indulgence in alcohol for example. Thus we see that in a very short space of discussing this problem rather loosely we get into the area of philosophy.

The problem of getting into philosophy is that it starts you out on an infinite train of questions that lead to some ultimate question such as "Who created god?" or "What do you mean by what do you mean?" Nevertheless, it might be a useful exercise to flirt with a few of the ideas that have been developed by philosophers over the years, restricting ourselves to the concepts of cause and effect; otherwise it will all get completely out of hand.

The ancients

It is one of the great curiosities of nature that man developed a brain that was much greater than he appears to need for survival. It is not difficult to come up with a Darwinian explanation of the development of the human brain. Greater reasoning power would give the individual advantages over his prey, his enemies and his sexual rivals. Combined with aggression it would give a tribe greater survival potential over its neighbours. Development of the first primitive tools required great mental effort and experimentation, as did increasing skills in their use. Communication by demonstration and then language meant that a breakthrough only needed to happen once for it to become available to the community as a whole. The habit of teaching the young was a powerful force towards the rapid development of civilisation. This habit is widespread in the animal kingdom, but in man, where the period of helplessness of the young is substantially longer, it was crucial. Once a discovery had been made it was passed down the generations. The huge reasoning power required for these breakthroughs became surplus once they had been made and was turned to other functions.

An analogy is provided by the progress of computers. In the early days, when a new computer was developed all the old programs were thrown away and everyone started again. Then the concept of portable languages came into being and new software grew from all that had gone before. It was only then that the exponential growth of computing began. The brainpower required to develop the wheel from scratch was probably considerably greater than that required to come up with the General Theory of Relativity, and its impact on human progress was certainly greater. Once any intelligent man had seen a wheel in action, however, it was a simple matter to reproduce it. We often tend to downplay the truly great innovations in human history. It was, for example, the invention of zero by Arab mathematicians that made the scientific age possible. When Stone Age man began knapping flints to create the first axe and arrow heads, he changed the course of human history forever.

Thus man became a tool-maker, and as such he began to develop abstract concepts such as purpose, which do not exist outside the human mind. Other forms of elaborate behaviour have developed in the non-human world, such as the spider spinning her web or a bird using a stick to dig out insects, but the absence of reasoning and communication made these evolutionary dead ends. Experience led man to associate cause with effect. This is a very difficult concept, as we have seen, and even today many individuals cannot cope with it. Some simple-minded criminals for example seem unable to make the connection between their behaviour and their ending up in gaol, so they keep returning to that place. This is all related to, but not the same as, the conditioned reflex. A cat will avoid the hotplate once it has experienced a burn, but this does not involve an intellectual identification of causality. A man will see causality, rightly or wrongly, in trains of events that cause him neither pleasure nor pain. A cat, as T S Eliot observed, is more practical.

Even the primitive technology of ancient man introduced a new phenomenon – leisure. The use of weapons to hunt prey and implements to farm the land took the pressure off the relentless pursuit of survival and man had time to think; not a lot, but enough to allow his great brain to get up to mischief. Thinking in the abstract had become a powerful tool in the fight against nature. Associating cause with effect had been a beneficial development, so it became inbuilt. In his new thinking leisure, man began to discover effects, and disastrous ones to boot, which did not seem to have a cause. Thus in virtually every society man began to invent abstract causes for those effects he could not explain, namely gods. A whole imaginary spiritual world developed in all societies and this was linked in the mind with the physical world (the participation mystique). Every stone, tree, animal or river had its own spirit; a concept that persists today in, for example, Shinto, and variations of the idea of a priest or shaman always appear. Ritual is also a universal development in human society, again based on a supposed causal relationship, and it often reached extraordinarily destructive proportions, including human sacrifice on a large scale. Myth (which may be defined as the other man's religion) took a powerful hold and became the glue of social convention that bound societies together.

The influence of the new phenomenon of leisure reached its zenith in ancient Greece. Society had become so efficient at feeding itself in a benign climate that there was a whole class able to devote itself to thought. The system of slavery was a substantial contributor to this development. The Greeks adapted the various primitive religions from around the Mediterranean into an elaborate form with a vast cast of anthropomorphic gods. While Rome was rising as a political power in the last century BC, it was Greece that was to lay its imprint on western philosophy. The Ionian philosophers sought to explain the material world in terms of entities such as fire and water. The leading Sophist argued that nothing existed or could be known and discussed. The Pythagoreans were more interested in the soul than in matter, but Greek philosophy reached its pinnacle with Socrates, whose ideas were organised into a systematic form by Plato. It was to be Aristotle, however, who was to provide the dominant philosophical force for centuries to come. In particular he dealt with the new notion of causality. Until quite recently the word "logic" meant Aristotle's logic; and his version of biology, with unchanging species, endured until the time of Darwin. Aristotle believed that all knowledge derived from experience, but he did not always practise what he preached.

The causality of disease was necessarily a human preoccupation, as it still is. The Greek physician, Galen, had decreed that diseases were caused by an imbalance of bodily "humours" or fluids, and that they would be cured by bloodletting and purging. This philosophy and practice would endure until the sixteenth century, when it was challenged by Paracelsus, who was the prophet of scientific medicine.
In the Christian era, philosophy had divided into a variety of sects and heresies: Manicheans, Donatists, Pelagians, Averroists etc. A key figure in the fifth century was St Augustine, in whose theological writings is the concept that experience provides the way to truth. In the thirteenth century St Thomas Aquinas claimed that all knowledge derives from the senses, but that it is only made intelligible by action of the intellect. The dichotomy between the senses and logical deduction continued, however, right into the nineteenth century and exists even today in the difference of approach to science in, say, France and Britain.

The age of science
The rationalists (Descartes, Spinoza, Leibnitz etc.) put the emphasis on reasoning. The source and test of knowledge was a system of deductions based on a restricted set of axioms, rather like the geometry of Euclid. The empiricists (Bacon, Locke, Hume, Russell etc.) on the other hand, made sense perception the central source and test of knowledge.

For our purposes, the age of science may be said to have started with Francis Bacon at the beginning of the seventeenth century (though it had been clearly adumbrated by his namesake, Roger Bacon, four centuries earlier) and ended four hundred years later in the latter part of the twentieth century. Philosophy had been frozen by the church for centuries and was largely based on Aristotle. Bacon broke the barrier of dogma that had produced this impasse in human thought and gave birth to the scientific era with his pioneering of observation and the use of inductive logic rather than deduction from immutable premises. It was towards the end of the century that John Locke gave systematic form to the ideas of Bacon and in particular to the operation of cause and effect. He was much concerned with the idea of relations and how they are constrained by the language we use. He observed that all descriptive terms, such as old or big, are related to our experience of the world and are not absolutes. Equally, cause and effect are understood only with respect to that experience and cannot by investigated from a dogmatic and deductive perspective. Locke was followed by the Scottish philosopher, David Hume, who put even greater emphasis on cause and effect:

> "All reasonings concerning matter of fact seem to be founded on the relation of Cause and Effect. By means of that relation alone we can go beyond the evidence of our memory and senses. If you were to ask a man, why he believes any matter of fact, which is absent; for instance, that his friend is in the country, or in France; he would give you a reason; and this reason would be some other fact; as a letter received from him, or the knowledge of his former resolutions and promises. A man finding a watch or any other machine in a desert island, would conclude that there had once been men in that island."

Hume's great contribution was to warn against the over-reliance on reason as a determinant of the relation between cause and effect. His emphasis on experience was to provide the foundation stone for the great edifice of experimental science that was to follow. He also introduced a healthy scepticism that was to dominate human thought. He appreciated that knowledge did not suddenly appear by dint of human reasoning, but grew from shared experiences:

> "Suppose a person, though endowed with the strongest faculties of reason and reflection, to be brought on a sudden into this world; he would, indeed, immediately observe a continual succession of objects, and one event following another; but he would not be able to discover anything farther. He would not, at first, by any reasoning, be able to reach the idea of cause and effect; since the particular powers, by which all natural operations are performed, never appear to the senses; nor is it reasonable to conclude, merely because one event, in one instance, precedes another, that therefore the one is the cause, the other the effect. Their conjunction may be arbitrary and casual. There may be no reason to infer the existence of one from the appearance of the other. And in a word, such a person, without more experience, could never employ his conjecture or reasoning concerning any

matter of fact, or be assured of anything beyond what was immediately present to his memory and senses."

The empiricists had introduced the idea of inductive logic, a process of reasoning from the particular to the general as opposed to the traditional process of deduction. The basis of induction is the assumption that if something is true in a number of observed instances, then it is also true in similar, but unobserved, instances. This development was at once a great liberator and a great hazard, since the probability of accuracy depends on the number of instances observed. It opened the way to the enormous growth of experimental science, with considerable benefits to mankind, but it was also to lead to the more dubious judgments that are our present topic.

Parameters and Variables

Variables are the very stuff of mathematics. When we write an equation, such as $y=1/x$ for a rectangular hyperbola, we define a relationship between the two quantities x and y such that for any numerical value of x there is a unique corresponding value of y. By convention x is known as the independent variable (the abscissa) and is plotted against the horizontal axis of a two-dimensional (Cartesian) set of coordinates. The dependent variable, y, is plotted vertically (the ordinate). This in no way implies that x is the cause of y and for mathematical purposes the hyperbola can be defined as $x=1/y$.

Parameter is one of those words that cause great difficulties of communication between the mathematical scientists and the social scientists. To a mathematician a parameter is a constant that defines a curve and different constants define different curves. Thus the equation $y=a/x$ defines a family of parallel hyperbolae, each one distinguished by the value of its parameter, a. Again this does not imply any sort of causal relationship and the division into variables and parameters is often one of arbitrary choice. The same relationship, for example, could be used to define a series of straight lines $a=xy$, where a is plotted against y, and x is a parameter that defines the different lines, all crossing at the origin.

All this causes no problem for the mathematically trained, but it is a trap for the layman, which is sometimes deliberately used to mislead; for it is natural to assume that the horizontal axis represents the cause and the vertical axis the effect, whereas the choice of which is which may be quite arbitrary.

Correlation and Causality

One of the greatest contributions to confusion and a tool for deliberate deception is the question of correlation and causality. A statement that needs to be repeated over and over again is that **Correlation is not Causation.** Many papers in scientific journals, and particularly those in epidemiology, establish that there is a relationship between two variables A and B. B is then plotted against A and there is a firm implication that B is caused by A. This is particularly rife among health professionals and gurus. We are told, for example, that there is a correlation between arthritis and obesity, with the strong implication that fat people are more likely to get arthritis. In one case at least (this author) the arthritis came first and the fatness came as a consequence of having to give up a vigorous sporting life. This is one common example of the correlation fallacy, saying that B is caused by A, whereas in fact A is caused by B. The other common case is where A and B are both the effects of a third cause, C. Many societal problems, for example, are fashionably ascribed to poverty, whereas poverty itself is equally a symptom of other causes, such as history, culture, education, intelligence etc.

Heat and temperature

Heat plays a crucial role in cause and effect. In fact it could be claimed that heat is the fundamental cause; for at absolute zero there are no effects, nothing happens. Whether stuff happens largely depends on the relationship between the amount the fundamental particles of matter bounce about, which is measured by temperature, and the height of some energy barrier. Thus the water in your kettle is held there by gravitational force and the forces that bind the water molecules together. As the kettle heats up, the water molecules bounce around more and more, until some of them have sufficient energy to overcome the barrier of the restraining force and are able to escape as steam. The crucial number that determines how many molecules have sufficient energy to escape is the ratio: (average amount of bounce)/(height of barrier).

The actual amount of bouncing energy is related to the absolute temperature, T, by Botzmann's constant, k, and is equal to kT. Almost everywhere in physics and chemistry we find the Botzmann factor, which is an exponential function of the ratio of the potential energy and kT, which is the thermal bouncing energy. For example, and there is no need for non-mathematicians to take fright, the simplest of electronic devices, the semiconductor diode, obeys an equation:

$$i = I \exp(\frac{ev}{kT} - 1)$$

Where i is the current through the diode, v is the voltage across it and T is the absolute temperature. Everything else is constant.

If we fix two of these variables, the third is determined by the equation. There is no implication of cause and effect. We can use the diode as a temperature sensor by fixing the voltage and measuring the current. At a fixed temperature the diode can be used as a one-way valve, since the current is high when the voltage is positive and low when it is negative. T is generally regarded as a parameter and the other quantities as variables, but this is only a convention, and in the temperature sensor case the temperature is the independent variable.

Electronic engineers have largely given up ideas of cause and effect in their circuit theory. They used to divide voltages into electromotive force and potential difference, but this only caused confusion so they now just talk about voltages.

The reason for introducing what may seem an unnecessarily technical complication is to show that, in this simple device governed by a wholly deterministic equation, **cause and effect are simply not useful concepts**. One of the variables only becomes a conceptual cause when it is fixed by an external device such as a battery.

Newton's third law of motion

This law is another source of the idea of cause and effect. It states that *for every action there is an equal and opposite reaction*. It is not always clear, however, which is the action and which is the reaction. Construct an object of different metals. If the temperature changes the object will be full of stress and strains. These all balance, but which are the causes and which are the effects? You might say that temperature is the cause, but that statement leads to an argument that temperature is the cause of everything, since at absolute zero there are no effects at all.

A change in the weather might cause a bloom of vegetation, which in turn causes a booming population of rodents that are carriers of a particular virus and subsequently there is a human plague. This is believed to happen, for example, when there are outbreaks of the hantavirus.

The importance of the mechanism

Evidently, we could go on forever discussing the principles of cause and effect and, indeed, philosophers have done so for centuries. The crucial fact is, however, that there is only one circumstance in which we can identify precisely the cause-effect relationship and that is when we understand the **mechanism**. In the case of cholera we had nothing but surmises until the particular germ responsible was discovered. Then we understood everything. This is why real scientists spend so much time talking about mechanisms. They know why the second hand moves, because they have followed the train of gears leading from the watch spring. When they observe that the winding down of the watch spring is associated with the motion of the second hand, the very next step is to begin looking for a mechanism. If there is one characteristic that distinguishes real science from the abortions that are discussed in this book it is this – **the primacy of the need to find and understand a mechanism**.

So we deduce that the crucial characteristic of man is that he is a toolmaker. Tools of course are no longer just solid constructs, like the flint axe-head: in the trade that we are investigating here, there are a number of tools of a more abstract nature, and it is useful at this stage to examine some of them.

7. Tools of the Trade

Science is one thing, wisdom is another. Science is an edged tool, with which men play like children, and cut their own fingers.
Sir Arthur Eddington

In this chapter the most important tools of the trade of epidemiology are set out in alphabetical order, for the convenience of readers who wish to refer back from later chapters. It is not necessary to be aware of all of them at this stage, but some are essential for understanding what is going on. These are marked with a star.

It is important to note that some tools are used positively and some negatively. Positive use is fairly self-explanatory, while negative use relates to a correct rule or procedure that is simply and routinely ignored.

Age

The most important determinant of your likelihood of becoming ill, by a long, long way, is your age. The probability of becoming a victim of cancer increases by about a thousand fold between the teens and the eighties. Yet this is one of the factors routinely ignored in many prominent epidemiological studies, most famously, perhaps in the book *The causes of cancer* (q.v.). Typical is a study of second hand smoke carried out in Greece (Panagiotakos et al, 2002), which ends with the usual call for draconian legislation to ban smoking in public places. This is justified by the observation that the probability of a coronary increases with the number of years of exposure to tobacco smoke. This is not a surprising correlation, since both these factors are correlated with age.

Anecdotal evidence

A mainstay of epidemiological research is the questionnaire. These often comprise questions posed in the vaguest of terms or in a tendentious sequence. In the Greek study mentioned above, for example, the prime question posed was "Are you currently exposed to cigarette smoke from other people (at workplace, restaurants, bars or nightclubs, home, outdoors etc.) for more than 30 minutes a day?" The concentration of exposure was uncontrolled (and clearly widely variable) while the 30-minute *threshold* is totally arbitrary; yet, subsequently, elaborate statistical calculations are made on the answers. Needless to say, the results were not such as to be acceptable outside epidemiological and media circles, but were seized upon by anti-tobacco SIFs and sympathetic politicians. See *Data dredge* below for further consideration.

*Confounding factors

One of the major reasons why real scientists are so circumspect about the practice of accepting low standards of significance or relative risk (*RR*, *q.v.*) is what are known as confounding factors. Sometimes these are obvious, as in the example of age above, and ignoring them seems particularly perverse. There are many quite bizarre examples. In October 2003 there were reports of a scare generated by researchers at the Henry Ford hospital in Detroit. They linked treatment of babies with antibiotics to the subsequent development of asthma. They chose to ignore the fact that the antibiotics must have been prescribed for serious conditions, including lung infections, which might well be responsible for the subsequent development of asthma.

The most important potential contribution of confounding factors, however, is where they are NOT known. People who give a particular answer in a questionnaire might well share a characteristic that is not covered. An attack on diet pills, for example, might ignore the fact that the users are all overweight, a fairly obvious example. There must be many others that are not obvious at all, due to the complexities of the human mind and body, and this is one of the main reasons why so many contradictions occur in the literature of scares.

Correlation

Verbally, correlation is the property of two entities that relates to the degree to which they tend to vary together. Mathematically, it is expressed in the form of a coefficient formed from second order averages, so that a correlation of zero means that there is no relationship and a correlation of one means that there is a total relationship.

The most important contribution that correlation makes to erroneous conclusions is through ignoring the fundamental truth from the previous chapter that **correlation is not causation**. Two factors might well be correlated because they are both dependent on a third hidden variable. Thus we see headlines such as **Second hand cigarette smoke causes cavities in children** (March 2003). This conclusion ignores possible confounding factors such as poverty, deprivation and insouciance.

Sometimes the relationship is wilfully put in reverse as in the headline **Drinkers earn more, says professor** (May, 2002). **Earners drink more** would be at least as convincing, since politically correct duties on alcohol put it beyond the reach of the low paid.

Chartmanship

Stephen Potter, in his famous Gamesmanship books, defined gamesmanship as the art of winning without actually cheating. Likewise, Chartmanship is the art of using graphs to mislead without actually cheating. There are number of techniques available to the graphic artist who has the brief to mislead the innumerate public. The most elementary one is the shape of the graph. If you want to make an increase look dramatic you make the aspect ratio tall and thin, if you want to downplay it you choose a short fat shape. One of the most widely used methods is suppression of the zero. What looks like an enormous variation of some quantity in a graph published in a newspaper becomes a flat line when numbers right down to zero are included.

*Data dredge

When a scientist wishes to test that substance A causes disease K, he can make a study of people who are or who are not exposed to A and compare the number of incidents of K in the two populations, thereby calculating the *relative risk* and the probability P that this occurred by accident. According to his lights he might deem the result to be a significant statistical association, but note that he has not "proved" that A causes K. It is a gamble, a throw of the die, which might pay off or might not. Not a very good bet.

Suppose therefore that he goes on to examine ten substances A to J and ten diseases K to T. He now has one hundred combinations of substance and disease. He therefore has a hundred times the number of chances of exceeding his chosen value of P. In epidemiology, this is more often than not set at 0.05.

Let assume that there are, in fact, no real relationships between the substances and the diseases and that it is all down to random numbers. If he sticks to his criterion the Poisson approximation applies and he can now expect 100P "successes", or 5 successes using the conventional value. What he should do, of course, is adjust his criterion to account for the greater likelihood of random successes, but does he? More often than not, the five successes are published as "scientific facts" and the 95 failures ignored, which is a form of *publication bias*.

Data dredging, however, will usually go even further than this. Large databases are often set up with hundreds of putative causes and effects. These lend themselves to retrospective "mining" for apparent associations. In addition to the fundamental statistical flaw outlined above, there are other problems:

> 1. The data gathered are often of an anecdotal nature. They are often in areas where people lie to themselves, let alone to others, especially with the modern pressures of political correctness (e.g. alcohol, tobacco or fat intake). People like to be helpful and give the answers they think questioners want to hear. There is little or no checking as to whether the recorded "facts" are true.

> 2. People are often equally vague about their illnesses. They might be either hypochondriacs or ostriches.

> 3. Many of the questions put to subjects are vague to the point of absurdity, such as what people have in their diet. Can you remember what and in what quantity you ate last week?

> 4. Questioners are liable to add biases of their own in recording responses.

> 5. Some of the variables are then calculated indirectly from these vague data, such as the intake of a particular vitamin being estimated from the

reported diet, or factors such as deprivation and pollution being estimated from the postal code.

6. There are often indications of reverse causality (e.g. people might have abandoned a therapy through illness, rather than become ill because of abandoning the therapy).

7. Often researchers disguise the fact that a result is part of a data dredge and present it as a single experiment, but they sometimes inadvertently let the cat out of the bag by mentioning other variables.

8. The subjects of the database are often unrepresentative of the population at large, e.g. they might be restricted to the medical professions or co-religionists.

Hormesis
It is a frequently illustrated fact (and an even more frequently ignored one) that small quantities of agents that are lethal in large quantities are not only harmless but can also be beneficial. This effect is known as hormesis and can apply to all sorts of "poisons" and even radiation.

Meta-analysis (meta-study)
This is a technique for trying to get a convincing result by combining the results of a lot of unconvincing studies. It is like trying to forge a strong chain out of weak links. It might perhaps be valid in some applications, such as well controlled randomised studies on animals, but for ill controlled observational studies on human populations it is, to say the least, dubious. The dubiety is compounded by the existence of flaws such as *publication bias* (see below).

Misdirection
This is a term used by stage magicians for business or patter designed to take the attention of the audience away from the location of the illusion and the fact that it is taking place. An infamous example is the age correction tables in *The causes of cancer (q.v.)*.

Mutant Numbers
This term was coined by Joel Best in his book *Damned lies and statistics*. It applies to numbers that suddenly, and often bizarrely, change their value or definition. A case where the definition changes is anorexia nervosa, a condition that mainly affects young women. The figure for the annual number of cases of anorexia in America was 150,000. At some point someone changed this to apply to the number of deaths, and thereafter this was quoted as the rate of fatalities. Since the number of American women between 15 and 24 who die annually is 8,500, the possibility of this claim being true seems rather limited.

Best starts his book with the "worst social statistic ever", quoted by a prospective PhD student from a professional journal: "Every year since 1950, the number of American children gunned down has doubled." Anyone trained in mathematics will recognise the definition of the exponential function and would be unsurprised that the consequence would be to produce a number larger than the whole world population by the 1980s. The whole farrago was caused by the syntactical and logical error of displacing two words in the original statement "The number of American children killed each year by guns has doubled since 1950". This is roughly in line with the increase in population and therefore totally unsurprising. A remarkable testament to the power of words!

Percentages

Percentages are often used to confuse the innocent and naïve (such as journalists). This is because they produce numbers that seem to be large, but are not. Thus a 90% increase looks impressive, but it is actually less than a doubling and as an *RR* (*q.v.*) it represents 1.9, unacceptably small. On the other hand, 90% as a proportion is nearly all.

Publication bias

It is an undisputed fact that negative and, equally significantly, indecisive results are rarely published (see, for example, A*n exercise in critical reading* in Chapter 9). Surveys have proved this, but the actual extent will never be accurately known. Even a casual reading of epidemiological journals suggests that the censoring of "uninteresting" results is almost 100%. This fact alone accounts for many of the so-called results of epidemiology.

Randomisation

As we noted in Chapter 4, Fisher remarked that without randomisation there is no significance. In properly conducted field trials of drugs, a large number of patients is randomly allocated to two groups, one taking the drug and another a placebo. The rigorous form of trial is known as "double blind" as neither the patient or the researcher knows which group he is in. Most epidemiological researches are not of this nature, but are what are known as "observational studies".

Ratios

Why do ratios occur so often in junk science? The answer is simple – they multiply the apparent effect by a factor that is always greater than one and is actually four where the results are least significant.

Taking a simple numerical example:

If the proportion of, say, boys to girls is even, then out of 100 children we have 50 boys and 50 girls and the ratio is 50/50 which is 1. If we have one extra boy per hundred, however, we have to have one less girl to make up the total, so the ratio now becomes 51/49 or 1.04. Thus the proportion has changed by 1%, while the ratio has changed by 4%.

The sex ratio provides a whole genre of junk science, with titles such as **Decreased sex ratio following maternal exposure to polychlorinated biphenyls from**

contaminated Great Lakes sport-caught fish: a retrospective cohort study. On examination they invariably turn out to be based on trivial accidental correlations.

Rodents

Rats and mice are used routinely to condemn a wide variety of substances as carcinogens. This is the prime example of exploitation of the *concentration fallacy*. The strains are specially bred to be prone to cancer (e.g. Sprague-Dawley rats, Fischer rats or B6C3F1 mice). These pathetic creatures, genetically programmed to get cancer just by living, are subjected to enormous concentrations of whatever chemical the researcher pins his claim to fame on. By enormous we mean **at least** 10,000 times what would occur in nature.

In October 2003 a baby food scare arose from the European Food Safety Authority. They found between one and twenty-five *parts per billion* of a chemical semicarbazide in jars of baby food. Why did this happen? It happened because instrumentation has become available to measure absurdly small dilutions of materials. All the vacuous ingredients of the health scare industry are there – mice especially bred to be tumour-prone, forcing on them absurdly high doses of chemicals (100 mg per kg of body weight), extrapolating the dubious results to human beings, ignoring the first law of toxicology (the poison is in the dose) and, above all, ignoring the fact that a billion is a bloody big number. In order to give a baby the same relative exposure as the rats you would have to stuff it with 100 tons of baby food.

*RR

Relative Risk or Risk Ratio (sometimes also called Hazard Ratio or Odds Ratio, but as the meaning of odds is quite different in, for example, racing circles, this is to be avoided) is at the very heart of the dispute between epidemiology and real science. If X% of people exposed to a putative cause suffer a certain effect and Y% not exposed to the cause (or alternatively the general population) suffer the same effect, the RR is X/Y. If the effect is "bad", then a RR greater than unity denotes a "bad" cause, while an RR less than unity suggests a "good" cause (and vice versa if the effect is "good"). An RR of exactly unity suggests that there is no correlation. There are a number of problems with such a simplistic application of RR. In particular:

1. Even where there is no correlation, the RR is never exactly unity, since both X and Y are estimates of statistical variates, so the question arises as to how much deviation from unity should be acceptable as significant.

2. X and Y, while inherently unrelated, might be correlated through a third factor, or indeed many others (see, for example, *age* above). Sometimes such *confounding factors* (*q.v.*) might be known (or thought to be known) and (sometimes dubious) attempts are made to allow for them. Where they are not known they cannot be compensated for, by definition.

3. Statistical results are often subjected to a chain of manipulations and selections, which (whether designed to or not) can increase the deviation of the RR from unity.

For these reasons most scientists (which includes scientifically inclined epidemiologists) take a fairly rigorous view of RR values. In observational studies, they will not normally accept an RR of less than 3 as significant and **never** an RR of less than 2. Likewise, for a putative beneficial effect, they **never** accept an RR of greater than 0.5. We shall meet later in this book RRs as low as 1.02. Sometimes epidemiologists choose to dismiss such caution as an invention of destructive sceptics, but this is not the case. For example:

> In epidemiologic research, [increases in risk of less than 100 percent] are considered small and are usually difficult to interpret. Such increases may be due to chance, statistical bias, or the effects of confounding factors that are sometimes not evident. [Source: National Cancer Institute, Press Release, October 26, 1994.]

This strict view of RRs may be relaxed somewhat in very special circumstances; for example in a large fully randomised double blind trial, as opposed to an observational study, that produces a high level of significance.

*Significance

This was discussed in Chapter 4. The two important aspects are RR (q.v.) and the probability of being wrong by chance, whether expressed as P or as CI (the confidence interval). The rather lax standard expressed by $P<0.05$ is so well established among epidemiologists that they often take it as read and simply state that the results are "statistically significant". It is important to be able to read claims of significance in terms of CI. When we read a statement such as (RR, 1.4; 95% CI, 1.1-1.8) as we shall, it means not only that the calculated relative risk is only 1.4, but there is a one in twenty chance that it is as low as 1.1 or as high as 1.8. It is this one in twenty lottery that gives rise to such phenomena as the contradictions quoted in the opening paragraphs of this book. Sometimes the quoted RR might look significant, say 3.4, but then we find that the CI is given as something like 1.8 - 9.5. Such a wide interval is a dead giveaway for a small study based on poor statistical practice and the unacceptable level of 1.8 is within the range determined by the rather lax 95% standard.

There is a complication, unfortunately, in that the "one in twenty" sometimes refers to both tails of the distribution and sometimes to only one. In the example above, if we look only at the lower tail, we have to say that there is a one in forty chance that the RR is as low as 1.1.

Toxicology

The first principle of toxicology, which has been known since the time of Paracelsus, is that **the poison is in the dose**. Arsenic is quite safe in small enough doses and, indeed, has been used as a tonic in parts of Europe. The most toxic substance known to man is regularly injected into the faces of the notoriously toxiphobiac women of California, botulinus. The popular scare poisons, such as dioxins or plutonium, are positively benign in comparison. Anything is poisonous in a sufficient dose; water, oxygen, you name it. Nothing is poisonous in a small enough dose; cyanide, strychnine, name it again.

It is important to note that the first principle of toxicology does not apply to living contaminants. One bacterium can become billions in a few hours. It is one of the ironies of modern mythmaking that the organic movement works itself into a ferment over negligible concentrations of manufactured chemicals, yet waxes ecstatic in favour of the use of animal faeces containing thousands of different species of micro-organism. One spore of *Clostridium botulinum* in favourable circumstances can lead to paralysis and death of whole human populations.

Threshold

A common technique is to compare two sets of data (say those developing a condition and those not) to see how many are either side of an arbitrary threshold of exposure to some "peril". This is fraught with all sorts of potential difficulties. If the range of exposures is narrowly distributed the results are highly sensitive to the choice of threshold and (in small studies) the scatter of the data. Using a threshold is tantamount to throwing away a lot of information. It is coarsening the histogram to such an extent that it only has two columns. There is also always the suspicion that the level of threshold was selected after the event to optimise results, so if one is used it ought to be justified on some rational *a priori* grounds. Thresholds are often chosen to avoid the *Sorites Paradox* (*q.v.*).

The other important misuse of thresholds is ignoring them when they actually exist in nature. No-threshold models are adopted in the study of various "poisons". This not only violates the first principle of toxicology (*q.v.*) but also excludes the possibility of hormesis (*q.v.*).

Trend fitting

Take any set of random points and you can fit a straight line to them (by the method of least squares). Take a few points from a sine wave (which itself has zero trend) and you can fit a straight line with a finite slope. The slope you get is a property of that set of points alone and not of any underlying process. It is quite remarkable how often, when you look at the evidence, that claims are based on fitting a straight line to what is little more than a random scattering of points on a graph. The "evidence" behind the salt scare is a good example.

Trojan Number

The term Trojan Number was coined by the author in the course of researching and writing the book *Sorry, wrong number!* The allusion is, of course, to the mythical stratagem whereby the Greeks infiltrated the city of Troy inside a giant wooden horse. The Trojan Number is thus one of the stratagems by which authors get their articles or propaganda into the media.

The major form of Trojan Number is the size of study. Early on in the piece it will be mentioned that (to invent some arbitrary numbers) there were 60,000 people in the study. The number experiencing the condition in question, say toe-nail cancer, is, however, much smaller, perhaps 60. Of these the number indulging in the putative cause, say passive drinking, is even smaller say 20. There is a number expected (as a proportion of the 60) at random from knowledge of the statistics for the general population, say, 14. Thus the number that really matters, the excess number of cases, is half a dozen. It is surprising how often an apparently huge study whittles down to an excess that you can count on your fingers. If the number 6 had been mentioned at the outset, the claim would have been laughed out of court, so it is never mentioned, though you can often have a pretty good stab at deducing it. In the statistics of rare events an excess of 6 on an expectation of 14 would be unsurprising. The rest of the 60,000 are mere bystanders. Furthermore, though it is not always admitted, these studies are often part of a large *data dredge (q.v.)*, in which many combinations of condition and potential cause are covered, so that the inevitable coincidental excesses can be identified and claimed as significant.

There are other forms of Trojan Number. A favourite is the *recycler*. Some new statistic is presented, say 63.21% of passive drinkers are depressed. That gives you the headline and a couple of sentences. The rest of the article is then exactly the same as the one you read last month with the same propaganda (and the month before that and the month before...). This way the zealots get their invented numbers drummed into the popular conscience or academics get a bit more glory via the institution's public relations office.

A variation on the recycler is the *ignorance statistic* – 72.45% of women under 35 are unaware that passive drinking causes toe-nail cancer – followed, of course, by the same old propaganda. And so on...

Virtual body count
There is nothing like a headline such as **Thousands to die of**... or **Thousands of lives could be saved if**... to excite sub-editors. Usually, when you look at the evidence you find that it comprises the fitting of a *trend* to a few scattered points of a graph that has nothing to do with death, followed by a tenuous chain of dubious deductions. Again, the "evidence" behind the salt scare is a good example.

Weasel words
According to *Chambers Dictionary* a weasel word is one that makes a statement vague or misleading. In the media reporting of epidemiological scares they are the words that try to make something out of nothing but in doing so give the game away. One group to look for is those that reveal the MMC disease (*may, might, could*). These short words, which have occasionally been emphasised in what comes later, are redolent with meaning. They say to us "These results are pretty tacky. In fact they are downright insignificant. But we are publishing them anyway for a bit of a cheap thrill." There are longer phrases that serve the same purpose – *is*

linked to, *is tied to* etc. Then there is the absent provenance – *researches reveal, recommended maximum intake, experts agree, can be attributed to* etc. One sentence that we shall see repeated over and over again is **More research is needed**. Basically it means "these results are pretty inconclusive". From the researcher it means "Please keep giving us more of the taxpayers' money" while from the monitors it means "We haven't the courage to call a spade a spade."

There are many other forms in the various manifestations of junk science, but these are the main ones in epidemiology.

8. Fallacies

Only two things are infinite, the universe and human stupidity, and I'm not sure about the former.
Albert Einstein

While the mainstay of junk epidemiology is debased statistical argument, many of the scares (and their converse, miracle cures) are supported by fallacious logical argument. Unfortunately, the days are long gone when logic formed a basic part of the general curriculum, which is a boon to politicians and other professional misleaders. It is useful at this point to list some of the most exploited fallacies and to add a few that are especially relevant to the subject in hand.

The original list

These fallacies were dealt with in detail in the earlier book *(Sorry, Chapter 3)*. They are briefly summarized here for completeness.

False dilemma

Alternatives are offered when in fact there are more than two options.
Example: Either sign the pledge or become a hopeless alcoholic.

Argument from ignorance (Argumentum ad ignorantiam)

Citing absence of evidence as proof of a favoured proposition.
Example: They cannot prove that GM foods are safe, so they are probably dangerous.

Post hoc fallacy

Citing order of events in time as proof of causality.
Example: the condition occurred after the vaccination and was therefore caused by it.

Personal attacks (argumentum ad hominem)

Losing the argument therefore attacking the arguer.
Example: All our critics are in the pay of the tobacco/alcohol/energy/drug industries.

Appeal to Authority (argumentum ad verecundiam)

Quoting from a claimed expert, who might not be qualified to give an opinion.
Example: Al Gore and John Prescott affirm the truth of Global Warming.

Anonymous Authority

Appealing to expertise that is unidentified.
Example: The recommended maximum is 21 units.

Complex Question

Two otherwise unrelated points are conjoined and treated as a single proposition, to be accepted or rejected both together, when in reality one is acceptable while the other might not be.

Example: Do you want your children to grow up healthy and free from man-made chemicals?

Non sequitur
The next two fallacies are examples the *non sequitur* (it does not follow):

Affirming the Consequent
This is any argument of the following form:
If A then B
B
Therefore, A
Example: If teaching improves, more students will pass their exams. More students are passing their exams. Therefore teaching has improved.

Denying the Antecedent
This is any argument of the following form:
If A then B
Not A
Therefore, Not B
Example: If you come into contact with carcinogenic chemicals you will get cancer. California has banned carcinogenic chemicals. Therefore Californians do not get cancer.

Fundamental food fallacy
Ignoring the fact that all foods are broken down into their constituent parts by the digestive system to be reassembled as the body requires.
Example: If you eat no fat you will not get fat.

Reification
If you can give something a name it must exist.
Example: The eternal hunt for Extra Sensory Perception.

Linear extrapolation
Given one point on the cause/effect graph, assuming that the relationship is a straight line passing through the origin. This almost never occurs in nature. Also sometimes known as the zero-threshold fallacy. The next two fallacies are examples.

The concentration fallacy
Treating toxic effects as independent of concentration.
Example: Almost any chemical given to specially bred tumour-prone rats in enormous concentrations will produce tumours, therefore almost all chemicals are human carcinogens.

The dosage fallacy
Implying that, because something given in a high dose is poisonous, it is also poisonous in small doses.

Example: People die of alcoholic poisoning, therefore that glass of wine is deadly.

The independence fallacy

Ignoring the fact that, when numbers are constrained to add up to a constant, if one changes others must change.

Example: Everybody dies, so the more we conquer infectious disease the more deaths there will be from cancer and heart disease. Yet the increase is treated as a mystery.

Gamblers' fallacy

Assuming that past events affect the probabilities of future events.

Example: The number 3 has come up in the lottery four weeks running, so it will not appear this week.

Further fallacies

The correlation fallacy

We have said this more than once already and will say it again. **Correlation is not causation**. Ignoring this evident truth gives rise to much of the fallacious reporting of epidemiological research. There are many examples throughout this book. See, for example, *An exercise in critical reading* in the following chapter. Sometimes the researchers do not make the claim themselves, but do not raise objections when the media do it for them.

In March 2003 researchers found a correlation between passive smoking and dental decay in children. Needless to say, the numbers indicated an unacceptable level of significance *(RR, 1.4; 95% CI, 1.1-1.8)* and, of course, confounding factors were completely ignored. Some of the startling headlines that were generated are quoted in the chapter on tobacco.

The birthday fallacy (and clusters)

One of the many beautiful aspects of mathematics is that an application in one area can be applied to an apparently unrelated one by analogy. An age old conundrum is "How many children would you need in a classroom for there to be an evens chance of two of them having the same birthday?" Most people would plump for an answer of about half (or even twice) 365, but this is an attempt to answer a different question, namely "How many would you require for an evens chance of two birthdays occurring on a specific date?" In fact, the correct answer is just 23.

Here is an explanation of the calculation from a fine web site for schools:

> For one person, there are 365 distinct birthdays.
> For two people, there are 364 different ways that the second could have a birthday without matching the first.
> If there is no match after two people, the third person has 363 different birthdays that do not match the other two. So, the probability of a match is $1 - (365)(364)(363)/(365)(365)(365)$.

This leads to the following formula for calculating the probability of a match with N birthdays is 1 - (365)(364)(363)...(365 - N + 1)/(365)^N.

As we saw in chapter 3, John Snow's cluster was a respectable few hundred, but under the pressure of the media for newer scares the size of a cluster came down and down until it reached a remarkable two.

In Disney's film *A Civil Action* John Travolta starred as a personal injury lawyer crusading for justice, naturally in the form of millions of dollars, against two companies accused of dumping chemicals. Allegedly, the chemicals contaminated drinking water, causing **eight** children's deaths from leukaemia; four times the average rate.

July 2000 saw the height of the panic about CJD. At the time, ninety people had died of vCJD. The probability of two of them having the same birthday is 0.999993848, i.e. a certainty. In fact there was an evens chance of three of them having the same birthday. Likewise, if we divided the UK up into 1000 areas of equal population, we would find by the same calculation that the probability of two of the ninety coming from the same area is about 0.98. Yet the original Queniborough two were claimed to be statistically significant and the hunt was begun for more "linked pairs".

Once the micro-cluster was identified, of course, the search was widened to include people who came from "the same part of Leicestershire" to expand it to five. This is known in the trade as the method of the Texas sharp-shooter, who sprays the side of a barn with bullets and then draws a target round the most prominent cluster. The cause of the outbreak was even identified as the practices of two butchers in the village, regardless of the fact that they were the same as the practices almost everywhere else at the time. Such vagaries are beyond the power of mathematics, but not, of course, of epidemiology. It was claimed that the number of times the victims were more likely to use those butchers than other sources was 15 (though in the small print there was a one in twenty chance that this number could be either a tenth of that or ten times it, but that's epidemiology for you.)

And so the search for clusters goes on, usually around the usual suspects of manufacturing industry and power generation. Most recently, pylons were blamed for the spread of the newsworthy foot and mouth disease, by a UK academic who believes that pylons are responsible all sorts of diseases. In December 2000, the microcluster was alive and well and living in Britain, the home of its discovery. "Scientists" discovered that **two** teenagers who developed vCJD received oral polio vaccine from the same batch of 80,000 doses. They were two of the five victims of the disease in the Southampton area. In the new age of unreason it is the story that matters and to hell with the science.

The extreme value fallacy

If you take a number of samples of a random variable and put them in order of magnitude, the extreme values are the *largest* and *smallest*. These extreme values exhibit special distributions of their own, which depend on the distribution of the original variate and the number of ranked samples from which they were drawn. The fallacy occurs when the extremes are treated as though they were single samples from the original distribution.

There are, of course, cases where the statistics of extremes is paramount. The *distribution of largest values* applies in cases such as floods or peak annual temperatures, and of course to all forms of record; while the *distribution of smallest values* applies to strength of materials problems, where the principle of a chain being as strong as its weakest link dominates, or to such phenomena as droughts or the duration of human life. The rigorous theory has been fully worked out, starting in the 1920s with the great R A Fisher, but refined in the 1950s by the likes of the also great authority on the subject E J Gumbel. Despite this, engineers and scientists were long after applying the normal distribution to phenomena for which it could not possibly apply, such as the breakdown of electrical insulation.

The birth month fallacy

A very common example of the extreme value fallacy *is the birth month fallacy,* which recurs in the media several times a year. It usually takes the form of a headline such as **People born in July are more likely to get toe-nail cancer** or more fancifully **Cancerians are more likely to get toe-nail cancer**. What the "researchers" have done is look at the statistics for each of the twelve months, pick out the biggest, and then marvel that it seems large compared with what you would expect for a random month. The expected (or mean) for the largest value actually increases (logarithmically) with the number of samples from which it was drawn.

Here is a lovely 2001 silly season story from the *New Scientist* that was picked up widely across the media, which illustrates one of the more common statistical fallacies:

June babies have higher risk of anorexia

19:00 08 August 01
Alison Motluk
Anorexic women are most likely to have been born in the spring or early summer, reports a researcher in Scotland. The finding raises the possibility that a common winter infection, such as flu, may predispose an unborn baby to the condition.

"It's not the whole answer," says John Eagles of the Royal Cornhill Hospital in Aberdeen. But it could be an unrecognised cause of anorexia nervosa, which affects around one per cent of girls in the US.

The team studied 446 women who had been diagnosed as anorexic and observed that 30% more than average were born in June. As the average monthly births is about 37, the June number must be 48. At first sight this looks like a significant result (at least by epidemiological standards). Applying the binomial distribution to a random selection from a population of 446 with a probability of 1/12 indicates that the probability of getting 48 or more in a random month is about 3%. **But that is not what they are doing!** They are making twelve such selections and **then picking the biggest**. Application of the theory of the statistics of extremes tells us that the probability of the largest of twelve such selections being 48 or greater is **30%**.

Let us illustrate with a simulation. Using the random number generator in *Mathcad*, 446 objects were placed at random into twelve categories, and a typical result is as shown in the histogram of births against months below.

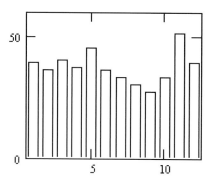

Figure 8.1 446 objects put at random into 12 categories

The largest value was 51 (in November on this occasion). When the simulation was run ten times the largest values were: 51,41,42,46,48,46,43,53,42 and 46; giving an average of 45.8. It is, of course, relatively easy to make the same point by mathematical analysis, but perhaps not appropriate in the present context.

This sort of nonsense appears at regular intervals. No mechanisms are offered, or at best ludicrous and far fetched ones. "Researchers" take some affliction, such as schizophrenia, match it against birth months and, lo and behold, they inevitably find that one month (or quarter) produces more cases than average. A survey conducted by the author in the village pub established that ordinary punters find this sort of thing ludicrous, so why do journalists and even self-styled scientific journals fall for it?

The end-point fallacy

One of the fundamental tools of *chartmanship* is careful choice of the range of the independent variable against which data are plotted (usually time). This especially potent if a straight line is fitted to the data points mathematically, since the formula for calculating the best fit gives emphasis to the contribution of the points at the upper and lower ends of the range. Unfortunately, in most cases in epidemiology we do not have access to the raw data, so are unable to detect the manipulation. The most notorious use of the end point fallacy is in maintaining the global warming myth, where the existence of the mediaeval warm period is an embarrassment, so they tend to start their graphs just after the end of it.

You do not need a chart, however, to exploit the end point fallacy. If you wish to "prove" that some phenomenon is increasing, you select your starting point when it is lowest and your finishing point when it is highest. Of course, where a fallacy ends and subreption or fraud begins is a moot point.

The Sorites paradox

Consider a heap of wheat grains. It is fairly obvious and clear what it is, just a heap. Now consider a single grain; is this a heap? Of course not! Now add another, so that you have two grains. Is this a heap? Repeat the process continually until you have the same number of grains as in the original and easily recognised heap. You now clearly have a heap, but at what number did it become one? This is what is known as the Sorites Paradox.

The whole paradox arises from the notion of vagueness. Like many things in this life, the concept of a heap is essentially vague. Now to politicians, bureaucrats, lawyers and certain types of academic, vagueness is anathema. They insist on defining the heap by a specific number, often quite arbitrary. They draw a line. In real life such numbers have no meaning. The hills and valleys of the landscape do not come with contour lines ready drawn on them. What happens marginally on one side of the line or other, however, can have drastic consequences. Whether it is the breathalyser, vehicle speed, size of lobsters in a catch or a thousand other things, someone has drawn a line to their own satisfaction and your life is controlled by it.

The Sorites Paradox becomes a fallacy when such an arbitrarily chosen *threshold* is invested with a significance that is not inherent. The literature of epidemiology is rife with such thresholds in the complete absence of any logical justification. In multiple form Sorites gives way to –

The binary fallacy

Talking again of thresholds brings us to the fallacy of black and white. One of my first clashes with authority occurred when a teacher decided to teach us some philosophy and logic. He took as an example of a paradox the famous one of Epimenides, the Cretan:

All Cretans are liars.
This statement was made by a Cretan.
If he is lying, he is telling the truth. If he is telling the truth, he is lying.

I said it was stupid to argue about a statement that was senseless. Cretans like everyone else lie some of the time. The proportion of lies to truth is a continuum. Later in life I came across an electronic device called a comparator, which puts out one signal (a "one") if an incoming continuous signal is above a certain level (the threshold) and another signal if it is below (a "nought"). The process throws away most of the information in the original signal. Binary signals of ones and noughts are convenient to operate on in a computer but the real world does not operate like that (it is continuous, not discrete, except at quantum levels). The first of our fallacies above, the false dilemma, is the verbal equivalent of the numerical fallacy that is Sorites. There is a grosser numerical form, however. Lots of numbers are put through the equivalent of a comparator, then all the ones are added up to yield another number that appears to be an informative one, yet it is actually the result of gratuitously throwing away most of the information that was originally available. The result actually obtained is highly sensitive to the choice of threshold, which provides a suspicious means of manipulating results. Thresholds apparently plucked out of the blue without justification are, to say the least, scientifically unsatisfactory and leave the lurking suspicion that they might have been chosen after the event to "optimise" the results, which leads nicely into the next chapter.

9. An exercise in critical reading

Not everything that can be counted counts, and not
everything that counts can be counted.
Albert Einstein

At this point in the first draft of this book things began to get out of hand. I had more than a hundred examples of junk epidemiology and it would have been easy to find thousands. The resulting commentary would have been bloated and repetitive to the point of being unreadable. It seemed more productive to take just one example of the genre and subject it to detailed analysis. The fact of selecting one, more or less at random, does not mean that it is any worse (or better) than any other in the *oeuvre*.

Here is the actual story as it appeared in the *New Scientist*. I have inserted reference numbers against the most obvious points for comment, which are taken up below, as this seems an admirable example to take for an essay on critical reading in epidemiology.

Electrical appliances linked to miscarriage

10:54 10 January 02
Anil Ananthaswamy, San Francisco

The strong magnetic fields produced by some electric appliances and vehicles increase the risk of miscarriage, claim researchers in California. Their findings also suggest that most previous investigations into the health effects of electromagnetic fields (EMFs) have been measuring the wrong thing.

"The studies really represent state-of-the-art research [1] into the causes of pregnancy loss," says epidemiologist David Savitz of the University of North Carolina in Chapel Hill. Nevertheless, he says the researchers' interpretation of their findings may be wrong. California is already initiating public hearings to discuss the findings.

One study was led by De-Kun Li, a reproductive epidemiologist at the Kaiser Foundation Research Institute in Oakland, California. His team asked 1063 [2] women around San Francisco who were in the first 10 weeks of pregnancy to spend a day [3] wearing a meter around their waists that measured magnetic field levels every 10 seconds. Overall, they found that women exposed to peak levels of 1.6 microteslas [4] or greater were nearly twice [5] as likely to miscarry as women not exposed to such strong fields.

More significantly, says Li, among the 622 women who said the measuring period had been a typical day [6], those who experienced high peak fields were three times [7] as likely to have a miscarriage. "That's another confirmation that the effect is due to EMF," says Li. [8]

Other factors can have a more dramatic effect, however. The risk of a miscarriage increases tenfold as women age, for example, from 5 per cent for women under 30 years old to 50 per cent for those in their mid-40s. [9]

Li's team didn't look at what was producing the fields, but appliances such as shavers, hairdryers and vacuum cleaners can produce strong alternating magnetic fields, as can electric vehicles such as trams and trains [10]. *The key is proximity to the source, as fields drop off rapidly with distance.*

Alternating magnetic fields also have associated electric fields [11]. *The few previous studies of the effect of low-frequency EMFs on miscarriages, such as one involving 727 women done in 1991 by Raymond Neutra's group at the California Department of Health Services in Oakland, have been inconclusive.*

But Li thinks this is because Neutra looked at people's average exposure to electromagnetic fields over time, not peak values. "People have never looked at peak EMFs before [12]*," Li says. "My study opens a new chapter for these EMF effects. Not just for miscarriages, but for other health effects."*
When Neutra reanalysed the data from his earlier study, which has only now been published [13]*, he discovered the results were similar to Li's. Women exposed to peak EMF levels greater than 1.4 microteslas were nearly twice as likely to miscarry* [14].

But Savitz sees things differently. "Both studies found a reassuring lack of association for the most well-established measures of magnetic field exposure, that is average magnetic fields." The correlation between exposures to EMF spikes and an increased miscarriage rate may be due to other factors, he says. For instance, women who have a healthy pregnancy are more likely to suffer from nausea. This may make them more likely to stay at home and do less, and thus also reduce their exposure to magnetic fields. [15]

After Savitz's comments, Li's team looked at their data again. They also checked for other possible risk factors such as drug use, carrying heavy loads and previous induced abortions [16]. *"We adjusted for 30 different kinds of risk factors. Nothing changed," says Li.* [17]

But Michael Bracken, an epidemiologist at Yale University, is unconvinced. "There are numerous ways of measuring these fields, and one worries that if you do it enough times, then you are going to find positive associations," he says. "There's a real risk in these things getting over-interpreted and scaring the dickens out of people." [18]

In the past, EMFs have been blamed for various other ill effects, especially leukaemia in children. But no one can explain how relatively weak fields might cause the DNA mutations that lead to cancer, and most studies have failed to find evidence of a link.

The peak values measured by Li are way below the recommended exposure limit of 1600 microteslas. Above this level, EMFs can induce electric currents in the body, which leads to localised heating. Li speculates that EMF spikes could cause miscarriages by subtly disrupting cell-to-cell communication [19]. *"But as epidemiologists, we should not feel weaker because we don't understand the mechanisms."* [20]

Journal reference: Epidemiology (vol 13, p 1, 9 and 21)

Here are the immediate comments:

1. What is state-of-the-art about this research? Weak field magnetometry is old hat, so are EMF scares. Time was when scientists presented their work with more modesty and less hype. As for initiating public hearings on such tenuous grounds, where else could it happen? They live on the San Andreas Fault or build tinderbox houses in deliberately unmanaged and therefore fire-prone forests, then worry about trivial exposures to chemicals and electromagnetic fields.

2. 1063 is the *Trojan Number*, the total in the survey. Those who actually contribute to the statistics are smaller in number and get fewer as we go on. The normal rate of miscarriage for known pregnancies is 12-15%, so there would be a maximum of 160 in the sample, who are then divided into various sub-categories.

3. One day is used to represent the whole of whatever is the putative critical period for exposure. It is rather unlikely (say one chance in 40) that the true peak was caught.

4. 1.6 microteslas is a very low magnetic flux density. There are no known biological effects at this level. It is the level you would experience one metre away from a straight wire carrying 8 amps, and about 50 times smaller than the earth's magnetic field; yet the description here is "strong magnetic fields". Anyway, what is so special about this threshold? Did it happen to give the best results?

5. If you wonder why magnetometers are so interesting to fringe science, it is because they are simple and sensitive. You see on television programs people claiming to be ghost hunters, who wander round houses thrilled to bits because the numbers on their instruments go up and down. Nothing to do with the matter in hand, but very impressive to naïve punters. It so happens that I published papers in the early eighties describing one of the first integrated intelligent microsensors. Magnetic sensing was chosen because of its electrical simplicity, allowing us to concentrate on the aspects of intelligence and communication.

6. "Nearly twice" means a *Relative Risk* of less than two, which is not acceptable in real science.

7. What is the scientific definition of a typical day? Is it the same for a dangerous sports addict as it is for a couch potato? This is what is known in the trade as letting the guinea pigs run the experiment. It has provided a convenient way of dredging for a data subset showing apparently greater significance. Those who had an atypical day must therefore show less significance (441 of them). Anyway, it is a purely anecdotal characteristic. The moral is, if you meet a pregnant woman, say "Have an atypical day".

8. Three times is apparently an acceptable relative risk, but one obtained by dubious data manipulation on anecdotal evidence. Assume a generous miscarriage rate among the 622 of about 15%. This means that about 23 were below the threshold and 70 above – small numbers compared with the initial *Trojan number* and room for many confounding effects. 23 extra were above the threshold, and the implication is that they should have been on average below it, but why? If you set the threshold low enough they will all be above it and if you set it high enough they will all be below it. **An arbitrary threshold is not a median.**

These calculations are of course simplistic and we are not told whether the factor of three is the exposure ratio among miscarriages or the ratio of risk ratios compared to live births. The choice will affect scatter and sensitivity to the choice of threshold

It is no confirmation. **Correlation is not causation!**

9. Age is clearly a dominant variable. Age dependent habits would therefore be major confounding factors.

10. The "researchers" did not look at the very thing that most real scientists would look at. An apparent correlation would only be the starting point in real science. There are many other potential sources of exposure; for example, some of the highest electric currents to which you are likely to be proximate occur when you start your car. Driving is then associated with all sorts of other potential stresses that might be considered confounding factors.

11. A complete red herring. Electric fields depend on two things, the magnetic flux magnitude and its rate of change. At normal mains frequency the rate of change is extremely small. Switching surges might be another matter, but they are not mentioned.

12. There are all sorts of properties of waveforms you can dredge for. They have not yet started on spectral analysis.

13. Why has this only now been published? This apparently innocuous statement is the most damning of all. It is suspected that one of the greatest influences in such "research" is *publication bias* (negative results are simply not published). How many other unpublished negative results are there?

14. Why has the threshold changed? Was it to optimise the results? Nearly twice is a *risk ratio* of less than two.

15. The possibilities for confounding factors are almost infinite. Did the women carry on working, possibly at mechanically and mentally stressful jobs, and did they receive their exposure at work? Etc.

16. More red herrings, such risks could not possibly be confounded with magnetic field exposure, but many others could.

17. They "adjusted" for thirty different factors, which is about the same number as the difference between the numbers above and below the selected threshold. What assumptions were made? Did they understand how their statistical package dealt with them? When epidemiologists inadvertently reveal the details you find that they use, for example, post codes as a proxy for deprivation, when there are multimillionaires and paupers who share the same postcode. Also, however honest the researchers, there is enormous scope for the human subconscious to intrude in order to optimise the results. In *Sorry, wrong number!* it is shown that even in purely physical measurements, the subconscious can act to "optimise" results. Anyway, if these risk factors made no difference they are not risk factors, so all the other epidemiologists must be wrong.

18. Couldn't have put it better. Interesting that the sane comments come from Yale, where the influence of Feinstein is apparent. He is one of the few epidemiologists who seem to adhere to the scientific method.

19. Oh yeah? Note the use of the word "subtle", which in epidemiology-speak means totally lacking in credibility.

20. A masterly quotation that sums up the genre. This was the attitude of the alchemists and astrologers. It was only when people broke away from this form of mental indolence that real science began. It highlights the fact that modern epidemiology is a throwback.

Among the hundreds of factors that epidemiologists and others have correlated with miscarriage are work-related stress, insulin, electric blankets, infection, abnormal anatomy, low progesterone level, abnormal chromosomes, immune mechanisms, amniocentesis, endometriosis, a wide range of medications, a wide range of solvents such as Perchloroethylene, polycystic ovary syndrome, alcohol and smoking (of course), poor diet, physical abuse, chlorination of tap water, chemical warfare (in Iraq), influenza, pollution, radiation, computers, water beds, multiple pregnancy, carbon monoxide, stress from "world events", folic acid, bacterial vaginosis, hormonal imbalance, eating disorders, Gulf War syndrome and above all AGE. The list goes on and on and on.

What can we say about such a list in the context of our exercise? First and foremost, if even a substantial minority of them were valid there would be hardly any live births at all. Second, if only a few of them are valid, then with such small numbers contributing to the claimed effect their random distribution among the groups in this study could explain the results quite independently of any other criticisms.

The Li declaration at the end of this piece is of major importance. It sums up the difference between modern epidemiologists and real scientists, so it is worth repeating and remembering:

As epidemiologists, we should not feel weaker because we don't understand the mechanisms.

As we have started with the foetus, we might as well have a look at some of the other stages of life.

10. Trials of life

Life's but a walking shadow, a poor player,
That struts and frets his hour upon the stage,
And then is heard no more; it is a tale
Told by an idiot, full of sound and fury,
Signifying nothing.
Macbeth

It was a new phenomenon when towards the end of the 20th Century researchers began to shape their activities towards the requirements of the popular media, but it soon caught on. This was all part of a massive social change. Institutions that had once been independent and driven by their own ideals and agenda found themselves under pressure to be seen to be "relevant" from the centralising forces in Government, Civil Service and the new burgeoning quangos (quasi-automous non-government organisations). Internally, Public Relations departments, the very idea of which had once been anathema, were growing in size and influence. Academics and other researchers, once only interested in the approbation of their peers, adjusted their programmes to accommodate the need for popular acclaim. As the older generation took retirement (often early and disappointed) a whole new ethos enveloped the world of research and the approach of the researchers.

The popular media had found that ordinary people had a number of obsessions, of which a prominent one was with their own lifestyles. An endless stream of articles by journalists exploited this tendency and the new generation of researchers soon jumped on the bandwagon. Many of them did not even bother with the debased standards of statistical significance adopted by the new epidemiology. Here is a selection, again a small but representative one, of some of the effusions from this new breed.

Before birth

Many of the stories told in this book can be treated as a bit of a joke. Some of them are more serious, in that they cause unnecessary anxiety to various groups of people. Perhaps the most despicable, however, are those aimed at expectant parents. Only those who have been through the experience can understand the intense anxiety that surrounds the well-being of the unborn child. You might therefore expect that people claiming to perform "research" in this area would exercise a bit more caution than they otherwise might. Not a bit of it! Some of the tackiest statistical chicanery occurs in this very area and it is all, of course, seized upon by the press.

Here is a prime example of the genre:

Vacuum cleaners linked to miscarriage yelled the front page headline of the *Daily Telegraph*. Strong magnetic fields produced by trains and household appliances such as vacuum cleaners and food mixers increase the risk of miscarriage by up to three times, according to a new study. The National Radiological Protection Board – Britain's advisory body on radiation – said the American study needed to be taken seriously, **although further work was needed**. "If true, there would have to be precautionary advice to pregnant women," said a spokesman. That, of course, is the one we dealt with in the exercise of the last chapter. Note that it is nothing to do with radiation, but that board was infiltrated by some of the most determined professorial bandwagon riders in the business.

Sometimes it is hard not to give up in despair. When one of the least hysterical broadsheet newspapers, the *Sunday Telegraph*, comes up with a whole page article, as it did on 23rd November 2003, carrying the headline **Spina bifida in babies is *linked with* cornflakes and white bread**, where are you to turn? It is all the more confusing because the author of the article, one Robert Matthews, seemed to be the namesake of the author of a brilliant hard-hitting pamphlet entitled *Statistical snake-oil: the use and abuse of significance tests in science* (published by ESEF). No numbers are given, apart from the Trojan Number, which is **almost** 1,000 women in the study and the fact that the offending food items **may** double the risk of such birth defects. Naturally, the main message is "more research is needed". The offending article threw in a whole raft of other epidemiological pap as offerings to the food fascists – 50 to 80 percent increases in risk of oral and ovarian cancers and, it goes without saying, obesity.

It is important, however, to celebrate the occasional intrusions of common sense that break into the media. The final paragraphs of the above article read:

> *Tanni Grey-Thompson OBE, who was born with spina bifida and has become Britain's best-known paralympic athlete, said last night: "These findings are interesting but you have to put them into context. Living in areas with heavy industry is also a factor, for example. It is really useful to encourage women to eat a better diet but there are also financial reasons why women eat what they do."*

> *Ms Grey-Thompson, who has won 14 paralympic medals and eight medal placings in the London Marathon, added: "There are a huge number of scary things that women are told when they become pregnant that can put a lot of guilt on mothers. Sometimes disability is no one's fault and there is nothing you can do about it."*

Even further back in the life cycle sperm is a favourite topic with epidemiologists. Among the myriad of things claimed to be associated with a low sperm count are asymmetrical fingers, salt, environmental chemicals (naturally) and smoking (inevitably).

Dutifully reported by the BBC (who else?) one report contains the exquisite observation that more than 40% of young men have sub-normal sperm counts. Here is some news for the "researchers" – **50% of almost anything is sub-normal**. It is, of course, the old endocrine disrupter and sperm count scam, which is like one of those round-bottomed figures that come up again however many times you knock them down.

The researchers, Skakkebaek and Sharpe, acknowledge that there is no firm evidence linking specific chemical exposures to human male reproductive problems, but a little thing like that does not deter them. On the basis of their lack of evidence, they argue for a re-examination of phthalates' human reproductive toxicity, for more data on exposure levels, and for studies of the effects of exposure to combinations of chemicals (i.e. more research is needed, i.e. keep giving us the money).

WWF, the global environment campaign, urged precautionary action now, because it says testicular cancer and lowered sperm counts occur decades after exposure. It urged the European Union to agree a presumption against the use of endocrine disrupters.

Birth

In *Sorry wrong number!*, a piece entitled *The Magnificent Seven* describes how portentous statistics extrapolated to the national population could be tracked back to just seven excess boys in the original survey. The target in that case was tobacco advertising. In a later one in April 2002 (**Decreased sex ratio following maternal exposure to polychlorinated biphenyls from contaminated Great Lakes sport-caught fish: a retrospective cohort study**) the target is that trusty old standby of the epidemiologists, PCBs, here linked to the proportion of male births. The magic words **Harvard School of Public Health** always suggest that we are in for something special. The article is a festival of numerical prestidigitation with many fine examples of the art of misdirection but, as in the other example, nowhere does it actually mention the number of boys it is dealing with. Give them their due, however, at least they avoid the usual sex ratio scam and stick to the proportion of males, which for reasons of obscurity they call the secondary sex ratio.

Anyway, trawling through the welter of statistics and adjustments we find table three, which gives us the number of mothers in each quintile of exposure to PCBs (of the order of **one part in a billion** of blood) and (if you will pardon the expression) the crude sex ratio. We can deduce from this our own table in terms of the number of boys:

Quintile	1	2	3	4	5
No of mothers	34	35	35	35	34
No of boys	24	22	16	23	14

From the totals in each row, we can deduce that the overall sex ratio is 0.572 and the expected number at random in each quintile is 20. Assuming a binomial distribution, the expected standard deviation would be about 3. Thus the number of boys in each quintile is within two standard deviations of the expected value; in other words the variation is insignificant. For simple folk like us non-epidemiologists a picture is always a help, so here is the binomial distribution for p=0.572 and n=35:

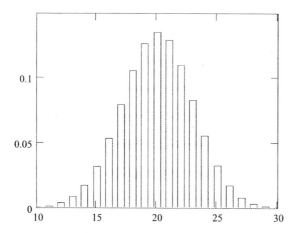

Figure 10.1 Expected random distribution of the number of boys.

Thus the number of boys, ranging from 14 to 24, in each quintile group of about 35 is just about what you would expect if you allocated them at random. From this numerical molehill a statistical mountain is built; complete with exponential decay functions, adjusted odds ratios and a startling claim of an 82% reduction in male births between the lower and upper quintiles (still can't hack that one!). Since the deviation of the number of boys from the randomly expected number does not even reach seven, this must go down as one of the eternal mysteries of epidemiology.

The next one actually made the banner headline across the front of the *Sunday Telegraph* (December 9th) – **Ultrasound linked to brain damage in babies**. It is more bad news for left-handers too. They are now officially brain damaged. The *Trojan Number* of babies in this data-dredge was (almost) 7,000. The *relative risk* for men who ought to be genetically right-handed, but have become left-handed on account of brain damage caused by prenatal scans, was 1.3 (readers of *Sorry, wrong number!* might recall that **Headline Man** achieved 1.63 on the basis of no effect at all). As many as one in fifty male foetuses **may** be affected (a risk ratio of 1.02). Of course the Swedish authors of the report in *Epidemiology* (where else?) had no intention of causing a scare merely to achieve world headlines:

> *Prof Juni Palmgren, of the Karolinska Institute in Stockholm, a member of the team, told The Sunday Telegraph: "I would urge people not to refuse to*

*have ultrasound scanning, as the risk of brain damage is only a possibility –
but this is an interesting finding and needs to be taken seriously."*

A favourite for the miscarriage merchants is coffee. Here is an interesting variation
from a group of epidemiologists in California:

> *Neither total caffeine intake nor intake of individual types of caffeinated
> beverages before and during pregnancy were associated with significant
> increases in the risk of spontaneous abortion. Unexpectedly, however,
> consumption of three or more cups of decaffeinated coffee per day during
> the first trimester was associated with a doubling of risk (odds ratio 2.4,
> 95% CI 1.3-4.7). Consumption of decaffeinated coffee before pregnancy
> was not associated with a significant increase in the risk of spontaneous
> abortion.*

> *This study does not support the hypothesis that caffeine intake increases the
> risk of spontaneous abortion. The association with decaffeinated coffee that
> was seen in this study has not been reported previously, and no causal basis
> for this finding is known. Since modern methods of decaffeination do not
> introduce significant amounts of potentially toxic substances into coffee, a
> causal relationship seems unlikely. Instead, the authors suspect that the
> association is due to bias resulting from the relations among fetal viability,
> symptoms of pregnancy such as nausea and consumption patterns during
> pregnancy.*

It simply does not occur to the authors that the observation is just a statistical quirk
of a kind that will inevitably occur if you dredge for enough factors.

Of course, they could not leave out the epidemiologists' favourite, pesticides. Here
is a contribution from North Carolina:

> *The study, which involved almost 700 women in 10 California counties,
> showed an increased risk of death among developing babies. Mothers who
> lived near crops where certain pesticides were sprayed faced a 40 to 120
> percent increase in risk of miscarriage due to birth defects.*
> ...

> *Scientists compared the cases of 73 women whose pregnancies ended
> because of birth defects with 611 control subjects whose pregnancies
> ended in normal live births.*

> *"Our study showed a consistent pattern with respect to timing of exposure,"
> said Dr. Erin Bell, who earned her doctorate with the research at the
> University of North Carolina (UNC) School of Public Health. "The largest
> risks for fetal death due to birth defects were from pesticide exposure during
> the third week to the eighth week of pregnancy."*

Thus the *Trojan Number* has not only fallen by a factor of ten to 73 women who were actually affected, only a fraction of these experienced the dreaded exposure. Then the sub-group were divided up into time slots, so we are back into single figures again. If pesticides come, can organic solvents be far behind?

They love to correlate things with birth weight. As long as you take the usual precautions, such as keeping the sample size low, there are all sorts of accidental associations that can be found. There is, of course, a high probability that the associations are genuine, since birth weight is likely to be correlated with all sorts of social factors, but the question is whether the actual numbers really justify the claims. Here is a typical example:

> *Babies born severely underweight get lower exam grades when teenagers. A report suggests rapid spurts of brain development during pregnancy and after birth are more important than social environment or quality of education. The research was carried out by academics at Liverpool University. The study looked at the GCSE results of 167 children of very low birthweight and 167 of normal birthweight who attended the same schools on Merseyside. Researchers led by Professor Peter Pharoah of Liverpool University found the normal birthweight group scored significantly more points for their GCSEs overall and for each subject studied. The normal weight group scored almost half a grade higher for each subject, typically getting a C or D, compared with D and E for the low birthweight teenagers. The normal group did significantly better in maths and statistics and got higher grades in general science, English and English Literature. Writing in the journal Archives of Disease in Childhood the researchers said: "The poorer GCSE performance of very low birth weight children, compared with their classroom matched controls, has implications for subsequent further education and employment."*

Childhood

The BBC's love affair with junk science has been an enduring one. **Parenting link to asthma** yelled the headline. The *Trojan Number* (of children involved in the study) is an unimpressive 150, but the proportion contracting asthma is given as 28%, which is 42 children. We are further told that those receiving "poor" parenting are more than twice as likely to get asthma (let's call it twice). We are not, of course, told what proportion of children receive "poor" parenting. Let us be generous and guess at about one quarter. This would all imply that about 17 of the asthmatic children received poor parenting against 25 of the non-asthmatics. The expected number among asthmatics if there were no effect, would be about 10. So the whole claim is based on about seven excess children. Again, readers of *Sorry, wrong number!* will note that The Magnificent Seven also turned up in two other fanciful studies. There's one for the numerologists.

Needless to say that it is all based on anecdotal evidence and value judgments on what used to be called, in pre-PC days, parenthood. The number of causes nominated for childhood asthma is legion, even down to one component of margarine. They never seem to bother with such factors as central heating or fitted carpets, however.

Vaccination

Only the very elderly now remember life before universal vaccination. Many of them remember childhood friends who died or were the victims of deformities, paralysis, blindness, deafness and other terrible consequences of common childhood diseases. It was inevitable that something so outstandingly beneficial would become the target of scaremongers. The egregious example was a scare that put millions of children in jeopardy, made a media hero of the prime scaremonger and put the epidemiologists in the role of the good guys.

On December 16th 2003, Channel Five television in the UK broadcast a dramatisation entitled *"Hear the silence"* about the putative link between the MMR vaccine, inflammatory bowel disease and autism. It was what the critics like to call a powerful drama, packed with stock characters, or caricatures, the determined mother in a lone fight against the wooden and evasive medical establishment, the sceptical father who finally sees the light, the evil international drug companies and mysterious forces tapping 'phones and cutting off research funds. The climax, however, was reached when the hero from real life made his entrance. They stopped short of soft focus and a halo, but it was reminiscent of the scene in Olivier's film of Richard III when the usurper Henry Tudor (played by the young Stanley Baker before he matured into the epitome of evil) entered in a golden glow to reverential music by William Walton. For it was none other than Andrew Wakefield, who had made his name as the author of this media scare, one of the greatest of all time. How this good, kind and wise hero contrasted with the cold villainy of the rest of the medical establishment!

There had already been a furore before the play was broadcast, with claims that it could cost lives. Wakefield's former colleagues, featured here as cowardly turncoats, tried to undo some of the damage (in the *Daily Telegraph* for example: **MMR scare scientist warns of impending measles epidemic**). Subsequent large-scale studies had failed to find any connection between MMR and autism. As Dr Ben Goldacre reported in *The Guardian*:

> *Dr Kreesten Madsen, of the Danish Epidemiology Science Centre, compared 440,000 children who had MMR with 97,000 children who didn't. The children who had MMR were no more likely to develop autism than the children who didn't. In Finland, one group looked at 3 million MMR vaccinations, found only 31 cases of related gut symptoms, and not one of these children went on to develop autism in the next 10 years. A group in London looked at 498 children with autism, to see if they developed it after MMR. They looked at when they had the MMR jab, and when they*

developed the symptoms or the diagnosis, and found no sudden blip after immunisation. Another paper shows no increase in GP consultations in the six months after immunisation. Two hundred children in London and Stafford with autism were studied to see if there was a new type of autism related to MMR, featuring bowel problems and sudden regression, a bit like in the drama: half had the jab, half didn't, and there was no difference in type of autism between the groups. In California, looking at 1,000 children a year, over 14 years, the number of cases of autism increased by 373%, while the number of children getting MMR increased by only 14% (from 72% to 82%).

It takes one back to an earlier example of the personality cult, here as reported in *Sorry, wrong number!*:

I had originally drafted a paragraph welcoming the forced retirement of an Aberdeen scientist, who in August 1998 had prematurely published the results of a botched experiment by way of a scare story on a television programme. It seemed a small victory in the battle against of junk science. I had, however, reckoned without the combined power of SIFs and the media. Quite suddenly in February 1999 the scientist in question, one Dr Pusztai, became an overnight star and one of the most spectacular media feeding frenzies ever occurred. It is an exemplar of the whole genre. The trigger was a presentation by a group of twenty scientists at the House of Commons. We suddenly had the junk scientist as hero. No fewer than twenty nine separate SIF groups combined to exploit the resulting furore. Politicians who tried to ride the storm were overwhelmed and panic legislation ensued. It was probably the most successful generated scare ever.

For the record, Dr Pusztai created GM potatoes by inserting a gene from a snowdrop so that they produced a natural insecticide. Then he fed them to rats and claimed that their organ development was affected. The facts that he had used only five rats and then announced his results on television without review did not endear him to the scientific community. Nineteen members of the Royal Society wrote a protest letter to the *Daily Telegraph*. A review of the work concluded that the experimental design was poor and Dr Pusztai was relieved of his post.

Who remembers Dr Pusztai now? But he served his purpose and the Frankenfood scare rolls on with growing success. So does the MMR scare and there is a real threat that the terrible diseases that once afflicted the children will return.

The world of work

A typical bit of epidemiology was a story from the US published in *The Times*: **Cancer risk for women on night shifts**. It exhibited all the usual clichés – Trojan numbers from data dredges, silly *risk ratios* (as low as 1.08) ad hoc theories and, of course, the mincing language:

*A number of studies have now hinted that night shift work **could** affect breast cancer risk*

*There is clearly **a need for more research** to clarify this effect.*
*Night shifts **may** also increase the risk of some types of male cancer, such as prostate cancer.*

The whole thing is a farrago of unmitigated rubbish. Why do readers of a once great newspaper have to put up with it? But there it is, alongside real and terrible events, dulling the senses and repetitively crying wolf, until ordinary folk are unable to differentiate between real matters of concern and empty scares.

Several studies had indicated that night shift work could be linked to breast cancer. From the *National Post*, June 2002:

Artificial night lighting may contribute to breast cancer because it interrupts evolutionary sleep patterns, according to research presented yesterday at an international breast conference.

Dr. Richard Stevens told the World Conference on Breast Cancer in Victoria, B.C., that a growing body of studies suggest the modern proliferation of bedroom night lights, street lights and headlights confuse our circadian rhythms and interfere with the human body's ability to produce melatonin – a cancer-inhibiting hormone the body produces mainly at night.

As no numbers were given, further comment is superfluous. Then there is good old Harvard:

Harvard University's Nurses' Health Study, which was published in The Journal of the National Cancer Institute last year, found a 40% increase in breast cancer risk among shift workers. Meanwhile, three recent Scandinavian studies on breast cancer risk in blind women found they were at a 20 to 40% lower risk.

The menopause
In many ways life has been unfair to the fair sex. They have to endure the discomforts of menstruation, the pain of childbirth and to crown it all the miseries of the menopause, followed by a high risk of osteoporosis with the resultant bone fractures, often resulting in death. It was therefore a boon to many of them when Hormone Replacement Therapy was developed. Not only did it moderate the symptoms of the menopause, it gave back their feminine self-esteem.

Such a wholly benign gift to womanhood was something to be extremely grateful for. It followed as the night the day, however, that it would become the target of the scaremongers. It was only a matter of time. The blow fell in July 2002. Here are some of the headlines in the British Newspapers:

The Times – **HRT is linked to breast cancer**
The Daily Telegraph – **HRT raises cancer and stroke risks**
The Daily Mail – **HRT linked to breast cancer**
The Daily Express – **Millions in HRT danger**
The Sun – **HRT danger for women**
The Daily Mirror – **HRT attack**

The "research" was conducted by "Writing Group for the Women's Health Initiative Investigators" and published in the JAMA. The data and safety monitoring board recommended stopping the trial because the test statistic for invasive breast cancer "exceeded the stopping boundary for this adverse effect" and the global index statistic supported risks exceeding benefits. The actual annual probabilities obtained were these:

Risk Item	Without therapy	With therapy	% change
Stroke	0.0019	0.0027	+42
Heart attack	0.0024	0.0031	+29
Breast cancer	0.0033	0.0041	+24
Colon cancer	0.0018	0.0012	-33
Hip fracture	0.0015	0.0010	-33

As we know from the *Times* article that there 8304 in each group, we can deduce the number of excess women with heart attack that gave rise to the whole scare was all of **seven**. That number again! It had a dying fall.

In this case, of course, the seven is an annual figure, but it led to a remarkable development in scare amplification by the *Washington Post*:

> *Each year 30 out of 10,000 postmenopausal women taking no therapy fall ill to heart disease. For every year women took HRT, they increased their risk of heart disease by seven per 10,000. This means that for every 10,000 women taking HRT, 37 could expect to fall ill to heart disease the first year, 44 the next year, 51 the following year, and so forth. While the absolute risks are small, the increases were viewed as significant, and women's heart risks escalated the longer they stayed on the drugs.*

You might come to the conclusion that these changes in the table are pretty insignificant. Hold on to your hat! In the actual paper that started the whole furore the confidence intervals for hazard ratios (i.e. *relative risks*) were given. Just take note of the numbers that have been emphasised in bold below

Results
On May 31, 2002, after a mean of 5.2 years of follow-up, the data and safety monitoring board recommended stopping the trial of estrogen plus progestin vs placebo because the test statistic for invasive breast cancer exceeded the stopping boundary for this adverse effect and the global index statistic supported risks exceeding benefits. This report

*includes data on the major clinical outcomes through April 30, 2002. Estimated hazard ratios (HRs) (nominal 95% confidence intervals [CIs]) were as follows: CHD, 1.29 (**1.02**-1.63) with 286 cases; breast cancer, 1.26 (**1.00**-1.59) with 290 cases; stroke, 1.41 (**1.07**-1.85) with 212 cases; PE, 2.13 (1.39-3.25) with 101 cases; colorectal cancer, 0.63 (0.43-**0.92**) with 112 cases; endometrial cancer, 0.83 (0.47-1.47) with 47 cases; hip fracture, 0.66 (0.45-**0.98**) with 106 cases; and death due to other causes, 0.92 (0.74-1.14) with 331 cases. Corresponding HRs (nominal 95% CIs) for composite outcomes were 1.22 (**1.09**-1.36) for total cardiovascular disease (arterial and venous disease), 1.03 (0.90-1.17) for total cancer, 0.76 (0.69-**0.85**) for combined fractures, 0.98 (0.82-1.18) for total mortality, and 1.15 (**1.03**-1.28) for the global index. Absolute excess risks per 10 000 person-years attributable to estrogen plus progestin were 7 more CHD events, 8 more strokes, 8 more PEs, and 8 more invasive breast cancers, while absolute risk reductions per 10,000 person-years were 6 fewer colorectal cancers and 5 fewer hip fractures. The absolute excess risk of events included in the global index was 19 per 10,000 person-years.*

It beggars belief! The programme was halted because of the risk level reached for breast cancer, yet the undemanding confidence interval of 95% actually embraces a relative risk of **1.0**, **that is – no risk at all**!

Naturally in the USA the vultures started circling immediately. Here is one advertisement that appeared in the American press within the month:

Hormone Replacement Therapy (Estrogen plus Progestin)

Hormone Replacement Therapy (HRT) is a common treatment for post-menopausal women that helps prevent osteoporosis and certain kinds of cancer. HRT typically involves drugs such as Prempro® which combine estrogen and Progestin, a synthetic form of progesterone. Estrogen, when used alone, has been linked to an increased risk of uterine cancer. When combined with Progestin the increased risk of uterine cancer is nearly eliminated. Together, these drugs have been used for years to treat the symptoms of menopause such as hot flashes and reduce the risk of osteoporosis. Common HRT medications include: Prempro®, Premphase®, Premelle®, Premique®, Provelle 28®.

In a July 9th press conference, Claude Lenfant, M.D., Director of the National Heart, Lung and Blood Institute announced the cancellation of a clinical study on Hormone Replacement Therapy due to an increased risk of invasive breast cancer and evidence that overall health risks exceed any benefits. There are an estimated 50 million post-menopausal women in the U.S. It's estimated that about 6 million of these women take estrogen plus progestin. Research shows that women who used estrogen plus progestin in Hormone Replacement Therapy experienced higher rates of serious side effects compared to women taking a placebo. These serious side effects include:

A 41 percent increase in strokes
A 29 percent increase in heart attacks
A doubling of rates of venous thromboembolism (blood clots)
A 22 percent increase in total cardiovascular disease
A 26 percent increase in breast cancer

If you or a loved one has suffered any of the serious side effects listed above while taking estrogen plus progestin, call now about your legal rights.

Statutes of Limitation Notice

All states have limits on the amount of time that can go by before you file a lawsuit (called statutes of limitation). To preserve any potential lega lclaims for allegedly dangerous and/or defective medical devices or medications, you should contact an attorney right away. Otherwise, you may lose your chance to recover monetary damages forever.

By October 2003, according to the BBC, 58% of women who were taking HRT abandoned it on the strength of this and similarly convincing studies. A nice addition to the latter report was this:

"But women should put it into perspective; one unit of alcohol a day increases a woman's risk of breast cancer by 6%."

That is a RR of 1.06! That one emanated from the doyen of epidemiological scaremongers, Sir Richard Doll.

Here are some of the comments quoted in the press:

PROFESSOR JOHN STUDD, a consultant gynaecologist at the Chelsea & Westminster Hospital, London, believes that the Million Women Study is deeply flawed and could endanger the health of millions of women. Studd, also Professor of Gynaecology at Imperial College London, says: "The study is full of errors. The women who have come off HRT after its publication have been given confusing information."
"The disgraceful thing is that the authors of the study held a press conference before we specialists in the field saw the research." Ambitious investigators, he says, wanted to make the best of their data before it was criticised and picked to pieces by experts.
***
"As regards osteoporosis, our view is that HRT should still be the first-line treatment. It is effective and cheap and has all sorts of other beneficial side-effects — reducing the risk of heart attacks in younger women, removing

flushes and sweats, removing depression and improving sexuality and well being.

***

"I recommend that my patients stay on HRT for as long as they want. I'm doing a study on women who have been on it for ten years and inviting — not recommending — that they come off it. All except one have opted to stay on it. Why? Because they feel better on it.

***

"Which HRT drug a woman has depends entirely on the symptoms. One dose is not suitable for all, and that was the mistake researchers made. The Women's Health Initiative (WHI) study had patients aged from 50 to 79 — 23 per cent were over the age of 70 — who were given a single treatment of a drug that we don't use anyway, so who is surprised at the results? The drugs that were used in these two studies were those based on horse oestrogens — Premarin, Prempak C and Premique — and we haven't used these for 20 years. Human beings best metabolise oestradiol, a human male and female hormone, found in other HRT products.

***

You're in your early forties, going into early menopause and your mother has osteoporosis. Your doctor says that you should be taking HRT — putting back oestrogen at least until your contemporaries start their menopauses. So what do you do now? One European specialist is even calling HRT as devastating as thalidomide.

***

According to Professor David Purdie, a specialist in HRT, menopause and bone loss, women who go into the menopause early should still take HRT. Purdie, who has just founded the new Edinburgh Osteoporosis Centre, says: "You need to restore the levels of oestrogen until the normal age of menopause." Failure to do so leads to risk of bone loss and osteoporosis.

An early menopause significantly reduces the risk of breast cancer, so by taking HRT you are only raising your risk to what it would have been. "Let's not forget that from puberty to the menopause a woman's body produces large amounts of oestrogen. Is it likely that evolution would have selected a dangerous hormone? No, so it's hardly likely that this suddenly becomes a killer."

By April 2004 the whole farce had gone through the full cycle and a new bunch of epidemiologists had exonerated HRT. This led to a giant banner headline in which the *Daily Mail* wailed **HRT: who can you believe?** By this time more than half the 1.7 million users of HRT had abandoned the therapy.

Old age

It is one of the fundamental tenets of epidemiology that everybody wants to live for as long as possible, regardless of decrepitude, pain or dementia. You can establish the untruth of this just by talking to a few people; especially those who have seen their parents die.

Old age is, in fact, one of the crucial areas of study in which epidemiology gets into difficulties, which it deals with by its standard method of ignoring them. A person of eighty years of age has about 1000 times the risk of contracting cancer as one who is eighteen. A similar calculation applies to almost all the fatal conditions, with a few exceptions, such as dangerous driving and suicide. As with any measurement problem, a very large factor associated with a number of smaller ones poses special questions. A one percent error in calculating the cancer risk for the elderly is ten times greater than the whole risk for a teenager. If the two are grouped together as part of a population study, a tiny difference in the habits of the elderly could well swamp the contributions of the rest. We shall see a notorious example with the book *The causes of cancer*, in which the authors chose to ignore this factor entirely. In an equally notorious calculation that produced the much-vaunted figure of 400,000 annual American deaths being due to smoking, eighty and ninety year olds were recorded as having died "prematurely".

The other major way in which old age distorts figures is the slow but steady increase in life expectancy. As more diseases are conquered and better life saving interventions are introduced, the average life expectancy creeps further and further into the range where certain non-infectious diseases are increasing sharply in probability. Thus, for example, brain tumours are increasing steadily in number, which interested parties ascribe to targets such as the use of mobile phones.

Here is one of those popular quizzes to calculate how long you will live:

> 1. Start with the number 76.
>> If you are a white male, subtract 3.
>> If you are a white female, add 4.
>> If you're a black male, subtract 11.
>> If you're a black female, subtract 2.
> 2. If you have a grandparent who lived to the age of 85, add 2.
>> If all your grandparents reached age 80, add 6.
> 3. If either parent died of a heart attack before age 50, subtract 4.
> 4. If any parent or sibling under 50 has or had cancer, a heart condition, or juvenile diabetes, subtract 3.
> 5. If you exercise strenuously at least 30 minutes 5 times a week, add 4.
>> If you do 2 or 3 workouts a week, add 2.
> 6. If you smoke...
>> 2 packs or more a day, subtract 8.
>> One to two packs, subtract 6.
>> Half a pack, subtract 1.
> 7. If you're overweight...

By 50 pounds or more, subtract 8.

30-50 pounds, subtract 4.

20-30 pounds, subtract 2.

8. High blood pressure, according to your doctor? Subtract 3.

9. Do you drink heavily? Subtract 1.

10. Have you received a speeding ticket in the last year? Subtract 1.

11. Do you sleep less than 5 hours or more than 10 hours a night? Subtract 4.

12. Where you live...

In an urban area, subtract 2.

Live in a small town/rural area, add 2.

13. If you work up a sweat on the job, add 3. Work behind a desk, subtract 2.

14. If you are over 65 and still working, add 3.

15. If you finished college, add 1. If you have a graduate or professional degree, add another 1.

16. But, if all that education has you earning more than $50,000 a year, subtract 2 because of the stress that goes with the job.

17. Are you intense, aggressive, and easily angered? Subtract 3. Are you easy going, laid back, relaxed? Add 3.

18. If you live with a spouse or friend, add 5. If not, subtract 1 point for every decade you have lived alone since your mid 30's.

19. Your age...

If you're between 30 and 40 years old, add 2.

If you're 40-50, add 3.

50-60, add 4.

If you are over 70, add 5 (and keep doing whatever you're doing.)

Now, which downmarket women's magazine do you think that came from? In fact none of them. It came from America's oldest and most prestigious university, Harvard, thanks to its Medical School's Gerontology Department. It is clearly unscientific nonsense, based in the results of accidental correlations and arbitrary thresholds. When published on the web it carried this health warning *This information should serve only as a reference to SOME of the factors that MAY affect how long you live. It is not a predictor of your life expectancy.* So why are they bothering to tell us about it?

So much for the trials of life! As throughout this book, the examples are just a tiny fraction of those available, enough to give the flavour without the tedium becoming excessive. But what about the other obsession of modern men and women, their bodies?

11. Body Parts

It is the Bing Crosby approach to epidemiological reasoning – in other words, "Accentuate the positive, eliminate the negative." Bing Crosby epidemiology allows researchers to find the effect they are looking for in a swamp of contradictory data but does little to establish whether it is real.
Graham Watt, University of Glasgow clinician

Of course, if there is one thing people are more obsessive about than their lifestyles it is their bodies. From phrenology to reflexology via iridology, palmistry and the rest, body parts have provided a good living for a great many charlatans. In modern times the tradition carries on, but now it has to be cloaked in a pseudo-scientific aura of statistical manipulation. As we have seen in other contexts, it is relatively easy to make a few measurements and find accidental statistical associations, provided always that you take the precaution of keeping your samples small. Here is just a small selection of the modern version of chiromancy and its relations.

Hands

It really beggars belief, but the *Sunday Telegraph* devoted a whole broadsheet page to a story carrying the headline **Is your son at risk of heart disease? Look at his hands**. It actually took two people to write the story, though why is difficult to understand, as the next day the *Daily Mail* carried exactly the same story obviously from the same press release. Junk science is always, of course, published by press release before scientific journals, that is one of the ways we recognise it. Regular readers of junk science would have remembered Liverpool University's Dr John Manning as the great expert on manual ejaculation matters: for it was he who in 1998 established that men with asymmetrical hands produced fewer sperm, and he did it all with a sample of only 60 men.

Now he was getting really ambitious and his *Trojan Number* had risen to 151, which is the number of heart disease victims he subjected to digital monitoring. Complete with diagrams, the article demonstrates that one's cardiac health depends on the ratio of the length of the index finger to the ring finger. At a ratio of 0.9 you are unlikely to have a heart attack before your mid seventies. At 0.97 you are unlikely to have a heart attack before the mid fifties, but at 1.00 you may be at risk from the mid-forties. There were, of course, no numbers given that would enable the claims of statistical validity to be examined, but it does illustrate our injunction on the way to become a successful media don: whether it is pylons, mobile phones, red meat or the humble salmon, the rule is to establish your gimmick and stick to it. According to the *Guardian*:

> **Attractiveness - it is all down to the length of two of your digits.**
>
> *A study by psychologists has discovered that people with the smallest differences between the length of their index finger and ring finger have a*

more symmetrical face. Facial symmetry has long been considered a key to attractiveness.

If the difference in finger length is larger, then the face is likely to be much less symmetrical (and uglier).

Nick Neave, an evolutionary psychologist at Northumbria University, Newcastle upon Tyne, released the findings at the British Psychological Society's annual conference in Bournemouth yesterday.

But note:

His study involved a group of 80 students, 30 male and 50 female. Their finger lengths were measured with callipers and their faces photographed.

The *Daily Mail*, however, which gave the above story a two-page tabloid splash, observed that fingers have been associated with:

Breast cancer
Femininity
High female fertility
Low male fertility
Verbal dexterity
Autism
Left-handedness
Homosexuality
Large birth size
Masculinity
Musical ability

Which all goes to show that you can associate anything with anything, as long as you are careful to keep your sample sizes small enough.

I thought I was suffering from delusions brought about by reading too much epidemiology when I saw a story about the relationship between disease and left-handedness, but it had disappeared from the BBC text service when I went back to check the details. Anyway, a correspondent from the UK reported the same problem, which made us both feel a bit better. Does this mean that even the BBC is capable of embarrassment?

Well the story eventually turned up again from Reuters (via junkscience.com, of course). It turned out to be from a data dredge conducted at University College Hospital Medical School and, indeed, claims that left-handers are twice as likely to get inflammatory bowel disease as the rest of us.

The *Trojan Number* (of people in the study) is 17,000, applying the stated rate of incidence of the disease, only about 50 of these would have had the bowel problem. Since only about 11% of people are left-handed, the expected number at random would be about five, so with a claimed risk ratio of two, the total recorded must be about ten.

Legs

One month it was fingers. The next month fingers were out and legs were in. The new daft data dredge came from the University of Bristol, whence one Professor George Smith told us that short legs in men are associated with a propensity to diabetes and heart disease. The *ad hoc* theory this time was that short legs denote an impoverished childhood and impaired growth. For the record, and as a sample of one, your bending author is blessed with duck's disease (short legs) as were his mother and father, though he was well nourished during early childhood. The Trojan Number in this study was 2,512 men in Wales, who were monitored for 15 years. These, of course, are the only numbers given in the press release and we are not told what is meant by such scientific abstractions as "short" and "increased risk".

Of course, if you want to grab the headlines, almost as effective as breasts are female thighs. The *New Scientist* reported in March 2003:

> Women with short thighs are more likely to suffer diabetes than their longer-legged peers, reveals a new study. For every centimetre below average thigh length, a white American woman was 19 per cent more likely to have diabetes. They are also more likely to have glucose intolerance, the precursor to diabetes. "We found an inverse relationship between upper leg length and the two metabolic conditions," Keiko Asao, at Johns Hopkins University, Maryland, told an American Heart Association conference on Friday.

> The Johns Hopkins' team analysed data on over 8700 black, white and Hispanic men and women. The average thigh length for men and women with normal glucose tolerance was 40.2 centimetres, compared with 39.1 cm for those with impaired glucose tolerance, and 38.3 cm for those with diabetes.

Nice Trojan Number, but you have to subtract from that all the men, all the blacks and all those who are not diabetic. We are not told what number you are left with. Then there is the marvellous ability to measure a woman's thigh to a precision of 1mm. How do they do that? Of course you could measure the length of the femur from X-rays, but that would expose all those people to dreaded radiation, and it would not be nearly as much fun. So, not only can they spot a three percent difference in length, but they can relate it to a physical condition. Perhaps the difference can be better explained by a leg-pull.

Breasts

There is nothing like breasts to guarantee grabbing the headlines. The media, including the BBC, duly gave the story from a Dutch team (March, 2003) a good airing. The headline was **Breast implant suicide link**. With a Trojan Number of 3,521 they expected five deaths from suicide, but got 15. At first sight, according to a rule of thumb for the Poisson distribution, this looks like a significant result. However, we have to take two other things into consideration. First this is clearly a data dredge, while secondly they have selected an extreme value from at least eight different causes of death.

Mind you, it is difficult to argue with the conjecture that anyone who opts for breast enhancement is some kind of nut. For the really ruthless seeker after headlines, however, there is nothing like breast cancer. The breast, thanks to the activities of tabloid newspapers, has achieved an iconic status that is even greater than it gains from the natural interest of the human male. Apart from the threats of disfigurement and death, the invasion of this symbol of a woman's sexuality by an alien growth is particularly poignant and tragic. All the better to get your propaganda across!

So, much more satisfying for seasoned number watchers was the item **Alcohol increases breast cancer risk** in November 2002. This carried the authority of no less a luminary than Sir Richard Doll, co-author of *The causes of cancer* and always good for a rousing, if empty, scare. It transpires that one drink per day increases the risk of breast cancer by 6% and, furthermore, every extra drink increases it by another 6%. A *relative risk* of 1.06 is ludicrous even by the standards of the most fervent of epidemiologists. The *Trojan Number* of women in the study was 150,000, but we can deduce from risk estimates given that the number with breast cancer would probably be under 1,000. By the time you have divided them up into categories of drunkenness, you are talking about a couple of hundred in each, so the 6% would appear to be based on about 12 women.

Let us make the fanciful assumption that this figure is correct. In order to achieve a relative risk remotely acceptable to real science (2.0), a woman would have to consume twelve drinks every day of her life. Unfortunately, she would probably soon succumb to brain damage and liver failure, which would tend to invalidate the experiment.

An interesting sidelight to this study was that smoking was not a factor, yet only the previous month the headlines yelled that smoking has been proved to cause breast cancer. Earlier on in the year the cause was deprivation, by January 2004 it was under-arm deodorants. Round up the usual suspects!

But give epidemiology its due. As well as the scares it also gives us the miracle cures, especially from Harvard. *The Times*, February 2003:

> **Eggs may cut risk of breast cancer**
> By Nigel Hawkes, Health Editor
> EATING eggs during adolescence can help to reduce the risk of breast cancer, a study says.

According to the Nurses' Health Study, one of the largest continuing surveys of health and diet, dietary fibre and vegetable fat also reduced the risks, but butter increased them very slightly.

The study has been running since 1976 and draws on details, updated every two years, of diet and other lifestyle factors provided by 120,000 nurses in America. The health of the nurses has been tracked, enabling correlations to be established between particular diseases and diet.

The latest results, published in Breast Cancer Research, an online journal, showed that women who ate, on average, an egg a day were 18 per cent less likely to suffer breast cancer than those who averaged half an egg a day. Fibre may help because it can bind the sex hormone oestrogen within the digestive system.

The authors make no comment on the fact that their results said that hot dogs, not generally considered a health food, are also linked to an 18 per cent reduction in breast-cancer risk.

Less unexpected is the performance of broccoli, every additional daily serving of which reduced breast cancer risk by 26 per cent. Butter increased the risk by 6 per cent.

Brains

Another favourite target of the scaremongers. Dementia is something that most people fear even more than death, so it is a cinch for a cheap bit of publicity, especially if you can link it with something popular like mobile phones. There have been various studies that link mobile phones to brain tumours and, inevitably, lawsuits in the American courts. The proponents serenely ignore the overwhelming fact that the hospitals are not overcrowded with sufferers from such tumours, even though more than half the population use the devices, so the tiniest probability would have such an effect. Some of them recognise this and make do with headaches or memory loss.

In 1999 workers in France reported a meta-study on the effects of parental smoking, which included the observation "The results on exposure to paternal tobacco smoke suggest an association with brain tumours (RR 1.22; CI, 1.05-1.40; based on 10 studies)". Naturally, toxic chemicals have a star part in many of the scares, especially if they can be linked to something as emotive as the Gulf War, as attempted by a Texan researcher.

A typical scare was splashed in the *Daily Mail* in 1998: **Poisoned plastic threat to babies**. It took the classical form – massive doses fed to mice affected brain development, while tiny concentrations were found in breast milk. Spokesman Dr Michael Warhurst said: "This disturbing research suggests that common chemicals, which can even contaminate breast milk, could be damaging the development of our children's minds. Breast milk is an important source of nutrition and health for babies, therefore Friends of the Earth advise that mothers should continue to breast feed. However, the Government must act urgently to ban such chemicals and reduce this risk." Not a word about the risk of being burnt to death, for the main application of the chemicals in question was as flame-retardants. Almost everything on the eco-theological hit list has been "linked" to brain cancer at one time or another (dioxins, semiconductor plants, Nutrasweet, magnetic and electric fields, ultrasound scanning and on and on).

Then there are the vogue diseases, such as Attention Deficiency Disorder (ADD), which causes 5% of American children to be doped up on Ritalan.

Then there is the obverse of the coin, the miracle cures. Fish is the favourite here. **Fish boost brain power** yells the *Sydney Sunday Telegraph* in a typical headline in February 2001. This is all a bit old hat, since the science was known to one Bertie Wooster long ago, when he fed fish to Jeeves at the time of need of great cogitation. Of course, the herbal suppliers will offer the gullible all sorts of nostrums to boost brain power. On the other hand **FDA says mercury in some fish could harm babies' brains** blared the Associated Press in January 2001. The FDA warned pregnant women and women of childbearing age about alleged hazards of consuming fish that may contain high levels of mercury.

Guts

The intestines are favourites with the anti-GM food campaigners. As we have already noted, it all started with the forced retirement of an Aberdeen scientist who in August 1998 had prematurely published the results of a botched experiment (based on all of five rats) by way of a scare story on a television programme. Quite suddenly in February 1999 the scientist in question, one Dr Pusztai, became an overnight star and one of the most spectacular media feeding frenzies ever occurred. It is an exemplar of the whole genre. The trigger was a presentation by a group of twenty "scientists" at the House of Commons. As observed earlier, we suddenly had the junk scientist as hero. No fewer than twenty-nine separate SIF groups combined to exploit the resulting furore. Politicians who tried to ride the storm were overwhelmed and panic legislation ensued. It was possibly the most successful artificially generated scare ever. Once the original research had served its purpose it was forgotten and the anti-GM campaign rolled on regardless of any "scientific" evidence. Nevertheless, the innards are always a good bet for scare generation. Again the hit list is rolled out as the cause of all sorts of gut problems (semiconductor plants, dioxins, Aspartamine and on and on).

Chins

Our old friend Nigel (thousands to die) Hawkes made it to the front page of *The Times* (February 6th 2003). **Close shaves beat death by a whisker** was the jolly sub's natty headline. If you want an example of classical junk epidemiology look no further than this from the University of Bristol:

> *How often a man shaves is an index of how likely he is to have a heart attack or stroke, according to a study in Wales.*
>
> *Men who do not shave every day are 30 per cent more likely to die of heart disease and nearly 70 per cent more likely to have a stroke.*

The relative risks quoted are 1.7 and a particularly pathetic 1.3. The whole exercise is clearly a data dredge, which ends up with a conclusion that amounts to self-parody. Bristol University certainly seem to have it in for Welshmen, who featured in the leg piece above. What about Welshmen who shave their legs? Nevertheless, the only accidental association they could come up with is between **frequency of shaving** and death by stroke or heart attack. Talking of which:

Hearts

Now we are really getting to the heart of the matter. Listen to music on any world channel and you will hear the words *mein Herz, mon coeur, mi corazón* etc. over and over again. Because the old pump reacts dramatically to adrenalin it is known poetically as the seat of the emotions and is particularly associated with sexual arousal. In story, ode or song, hearts get broken, leap, soar and perform other aerobatics. The heir to the throne urges us all to look into our hearts, whereby we will all become organic gardeners and talk to our flowers. The church invites us to lift them up and they take up more space in the index of the Oxford Dictionary of Quotations than anything else. Furthermore, most deaths, whatever the primary cause, are the result of heart failure. You could fill an encyclopaedia with the putative causes of heart attacks. Most famous is the cholesterol myth, of which more later.

> ***Nature*** *August 2002: A 16-year study has found one of the first direct links between a fatty diet and heart disease in women. For women, an extra 100 grams of saturated fat per week increased the risk of heart disease by more than a third. "It's clear cut," says lead researcher David Boniface, an epidemiologist at the University of Hertfordshire in Hatfield, UK.*

But epidemiologists kindly offer us a cure:

> ***BBC*** *May 2002 – Heart attack victims may live longer by drinking plenty of tea, according to doctors.*
>
> *A study of patients with heart disease has found those who are heavy or even moderate tea drinkers live substantially longer than those who don't have a regular cuppa.*
>
> *Research by doctors in Israel found heavy drinkers – those who drank more than 14 cups of tea a week – had a 44% lower death rate than non-tea drinkers in the three and a half years following their heart attacks.*

There had long been official hand-wringing over the seemingly relentless rise of heart disease, which had increased steadily throughout the first half of the twentieth century, doubling in that interval. It was crying out for that "Eureka!" moment, which in the late fifties was provided by one Ancel Keys. To cut a long story short, mainly by comparing different populations he established what he believed was a unique link between heart disease and diet, particularly fat.

Coronary heart disease has since become a favourite with the scaremongers and food fascists. Most doctors will put it on the death certificate in the case of a sudden unexpected death. The main reason this is done in Britain is that it is a way of avoiding the trauma of dealing with the coroner. In fact, when research has been done on the basis of post-mortems it has been found that such a diagnosis is wrong in more than half the cases. Ravnskov (see Bibliography) quotes considerable evidence that fashion as much as anything else determines the tendency to blame heart disease. For example, faced with the same written evidence American medics were 33 per cent more likely to diagnose heart disease than British ones and 50 per cent more than Norwegian ones. There are endless stories about the correlation of fat consumption and heart disease. In fact the disease correlates better with factors such as sales of TV sets and the local rate of tax.

The heart-diet theory has built up a huge inertia of vested interests. It has spawned an industry that annually turns over billions of dollars. There are drug companies, publishers of diet books (always at the top of the bestseller list), dieticians, sellers of "health" foods. Above all, there are thousands of researchers and physicians who have invested their careers and reputations in the theory. To abandon it now would be to pour scorn on their own life's work. These are no longer the detached scientists of yesteryear, idealistic or dilettante, who could put science above their own interests. These are careerists who seek fame as well as fortune and cling on to both.

It would be bootless to rehearse the whole farrago of the heart-diet theory here. Other authors (Le Fanu and Ravnskov, for example) have done so with great skill and attention to detail. Much of it was created by the continual repetition of *ex cathedra* statements with no scientific foundation at all; for example Geoffrey Rose "The modern British diet is killing people in their thousands from heart attacks" or again "Western food is the chief cause of our modern epidemic of heart disease." Any dissent was put down with contumely; Ancel Keys "Most of those who are critical have no knowledge of the subject whatsoever…. And many of them are self-serving." The latter was from one who had initiated the whole thing with a quite extraordinary act of subreption, as we shall see in the next chapter.

Here is Le Fanu's version of what should have been the death knell of this theory, but for the vested interests in preserving it:

> *Two final events finally undermined the apparently seamless litany of half-truths that sustained Keys's thesis by providing a much more satisfactory explanation of what was really going on. The first was the 'rediscovery' that the thrombus, not the levels of cholesterol in the blood, was the critical factor in causing heart disease. The second was the discovery of a*

bacterium, chlamydia, in the walls of the coronary artery, which helped to explain why the pattern of the rise and fall in heart disease resembled an infectious epidemic rather than a disease caused by social factors.

This observation was inconvenient to the scare-mongering establishment, so they ignored it and went on to tie heart disease to any of the usual suspects they could, even pollution and, of course, passive smoking. The list of target substances is a long one, so let us have a look at a few of them.

12. Substance abuse

What some call health, if purchased by perpetual anxiety about diet, isn't much better than tedious disease.
George Dennison Prentice

Since the dawn of human intelligence, mankind has attributed powerful and mysterious effects to various forms of matter on human physiology. Some of these attributions are clearly true, narcotics being a prime example, but in most cases the basis of the belief is no more than blind faith. Faith, however, is a potent force that, metaphorically at least, can move mountains; so much so that whole species can be threatened with extinction because of the tenets of, say, traditional Chinese medicine, which endows small parts of their anatomies with magic curative powers. In the literature and oral tradition of all societies there exists a panoply of philtres, ointments, remedies, specifics, antidotes and other medications that have little or no scientific basis. As the age of science began to dawn in the seventeenth and eighteenth centuries, however, such beliefs retreated, eventually being dismissed, at least by the intelligentsia, as old wives' tales. As soon as the role of germs, for example, was understood, the irrational nature of many of the traditional cures was exposed.

As we have seen, it was in the mid-twentieth century that this process began to go into reverse. There were many reasons for this. An important one was that people began to turn away from science in reaction to some of its more evil products, such as the atom bomb. Science, too, began to turn in on itself, largely through a change from being a self-regulating philosophy to a practical tool attractive to bureaucrats and politicians, who had goals of their own unrelated to the disinterested pursuit of knowledge and truth and who therefore took control of it.

The false damning or blessing of substances comes about by the action of a number of processes, either alone or more often in combination.

Amplification

One process by which this happened might be called amplification. Once a substance was identified as having one deleterious effect, it was branded as evil, and this effect was extended to a whole raft of others by a process of extrapolation. Tobacco, for example, had always had its opponents (such as James the First and Adolf Hitler), but once it was scientifically established as being a factor in the incidence of lung cancer, it was immediately a candidate for the cause all sorts of other evils. Alcohol, responsible for the social ills associated with drunkenness and diseases such as cirrhosis of the liver, was as a consequence also deemed to be capable of all sorts of other ill effects. Known stimulants, such as coffee, automatically became the target for investigation for a whole range of other possible properties, both good and ill. Vitamins, essential to healthy life in very small doses, by the process of amplification were endowed with many other favourable attributes.

Scattergun

Another process is the scattergun. The existence of the $P<0.05$ convention meant that if enough combinations of substances and effects were investigated one in twenty of them would come up trumps. Scientists could undertake almost any investigation and, as long as they had the required number of combinations of cause and effect they were assured of success (the *data dredge*).

Corporate momentum

Organisations of the type that concern us here (i.e. SIFs) come into being as collections of individuals who are fanatical about one particular issue – alcohol, tobacco, pollution etc. It is in the nature of such organisations that, once they are established, they begin to behave like business corporations. They take on premises, staff and other overheads, creating for themselves a cash flow problem. Like businesses they can only continue to walk the tightrope they have set up for themselves by increasing their income, and in turn manufacturing more of their product, which in this case is anxiety. The income arises from charitable donations or, in some cases, government subsidy, but in order to stimulate the income it is necessary to remain newsworthy. So the SIFs seize upon any evidence that appears to support their particular viewpoint and ensure that it gets the maximum airing. In order to do this they form symbiotic relationships with other groups. The press and other media are ever hungry for news stories, preferably of a scary nature, and are always grateful if these are served up ready made without the need for further effort. Scientists, equally hungry for fame and research grants, are encouraged to move into particular areas (and achieve appropriate results!), secure in the knowledge that they are guaranteed widespread coverage.

Political momentum

The alternative to the corporate strategy is for groups of fanatics to form a political party. In much of the world this is a sterile operation, but it comes into its own when proportional representation operates. Under these conditions single party government becomes virtually impossible and small parties can twist the arms of their numerically superior coalition partners to hog the ministries that correspond to their own particular obsession. Thus the Greens, for example, managed to gain a virtual monopoly on environment ministries in Europe and were able to foist a theory of their choice onto a whole continent. Having failed in the 1960s with threats of a new ice age, they did an about turn and adopted suggestions by some scientists that man-made global warming was occurring. You can find a scientist who has suggested almost anything if you look hard enough. The spurious theory of climate change is easily disposed of by scientific argument and the actual evidence, but by careful selection and practical politicking you can bring almost any proposition to the fore. The ease with which a specious theory such as global warming can be imposed on the world constitutes a textbook example of political chicanery. Once you have crossed a certain threshold the theory becomes established as fact and other politicians feel obliged to pay lip service to it. It can then become a political tool to conduct such intrigues as economic warfare against a competitor, and therefore convenient to maintain.

Where proportional representation is absent there are other strategies that can be adopted, depending mainly on establishing a powerful faction within an existing party. In the European Union control is yielded to unelected commissioners, which gives even greater scope for SIFs to take control of particular areas, most notably the environment.

Let us look at a few of the "discoveries" about particular substances, taking just a very small sample of the copious literature you can find on each. They are in no particular order.

Water

Every day there are banal stories based on silly numbers that are so vacuous that they are not worthy of remark, but when one appears on the front page of *The Times*, which used to be the newspaper of record, perhaps some comment is called for. Thus we find (January 25th, 2001) that "scientists" at the University of Bristol have shown:

How water on the brain can scupper quiz hopefuls

The actual story comes from the **New Scientist**, which used to be a respectable scientific journal:

QUIZ show contestants should refrain from taking nervous sips of water. Simply drinking water at the wrong time can impair our mental performance, say British researchers.

Experimental psychologist Peter Rogers and his colleagues from the University of Bristol asked 60 volunteers to rate how thirsty they felt. They then tested their reactions with a task that involved pressing buttons in response to prompts on a screen. The volunteers either drank nothing before the test or had a cupful (330 millilitres) of tap water, chilled to 10 °C.

People who were thirsty at the beginning of the test and took a drink performed 10 per cent better than those who drank nothing. But the "hit rate" of those who weren't thirsty to start with dropped by 15 per cent after a drink.

Drinking too much water might affect your ability to drive or perform intellectually demanding tasks, says Rogers. "If your performance is changing by 15 per cent, that's quite a big effect," agrees psychologist Nick Neave of the University of Northumbria in Newcastle.

Rogers thinks that the temperature of the drinks might explain part of the effect. "We like our drinks hot or cold. The body has to divert resources to deal with the local cooling effect in the gut."

Don't you just love the precision of the 330 millilitres and the 10 °C? We have sixty people divided into three separate groups, i.e. about twenty in each. If you still think that you can get meaningful results from such tests on a sample of twenty you are reading the wrong book.

What is more relevant in these enlightened days is the motivation for "researchers" to embark on a particular project. The fact is that quizzes were in the news in the UK. One was based on the new BBC culture of gratuitous rudeness and the other on the ITV cultivation of phoney drama. In the new university system, brownie points are obtained for hitting the headlines, so you go for what is in the news. What would Newton, Rutherford or Russell have made of it all? Worry not! Nowadays they probably would not have been appointed in the first place.

The *Daily Telegraph* announced the death of a woman from acute water intoxication. Could this be the start of a whole new bandwagon? **Number Watch**, whose author was somewhat in need of a nice little earner, decided to launch its own charity before the usual suspects move in. We were therefore pleased to announce the formation of **Water Concern**. Other titles, such as Water Action for Health or WAH!, were considered but rejected as not having the right resonance. So the slogan was *It's your WC, make a deposit today!*

Our first project was to recruit counsellors to offer support and advice to elderly Sassenachs who have unsuspectingly been adding water to their whisky, thereby exposing themselves to a risk of premature death.

But this is only the beginning. Even very young children are so addicted to this substance that they feel they cannot live without it. Even those who start recreationally on soft water have been shown to be highly likely to progress to hard water. Often they end up by going rapidly down hill on snow. By the time they reach adulthood many of them are hopeless aquatics.

So watch out for scary reports from our extensive teams of epidemiologists, who will prove that water abuse is associated with every disease under the sun. Support our dehydration clinics, where even the most hopeless cases get the opportunity to dry out. Above all, send in lots of money to support our growing band of administrators, who would otherwise be thrown out on the streets with their families. Make WC not just a public convenience, but part of your life. You know it makes cents!

Food in general
All over the British media in February 2002 there were stories about British fatties (who still had not caught up with American fatties by a long way). The culprits are unequivocally fast food and television. The origin was yet another audit. You can find it all in the Audit Commission's 72-page report. There is an executive summary

for those with poorly developed masochistic tendencies. 21 percent of British women and 17 percent of British men are now officially obese. By 2010 they will have caught up with the USA.

Regular number watchers found many old friends in the small print, including the Harvard Nurses' Health Study and other *data dredges*, *relative risks* of less than 2, correlations as causations, missing links, non sequiturs and costings with only one side of the balance sheet shown.

While possibly agreeing that fat kids are a sad, bad aspect of our modern society, readers might wish to consider a few facts before reaching a judgment:

> 1. Government and bureaucrats have colluded with the media and SIFs in hyping scares about paedophiles, drunken drivers and other perceived risks, resulting in children being cocooned.
> 2. Changes in legislation have fostered the rapid growth of the compensation industry, while health and safety laws and the concomitant snoopers have grown beyond reason. As a result children's playgrounds have closed down on a massive scale (e.g. every pub garden playground in great swathes of the country disappeared). A village playground was closed down because the swings were 60 cm too tall according to EU regulations.
> 3. Politically Correct local councils have deemed that competitive sport is inappropriate, which justifies selling off sports fields to become supermarkets.
> 4. There are no brownie points for physical education in the oppressive auditing and league table generation that overwhelm teachers and even determine their salaries.
> 5. Being "linked with" is not causation. For example, as mentioned earlier your author became fat **after** getting arthritis and having to give up sport.
> 6. Premature deaths do not cost the health service more, since they obviate the costs of geriatric treatment such as hip replacements and caring for those with dementia.

The recommended recipe is more bureaucracy, more targets and more league tables, the bureaucrat's answer to everything. The National Health Service is urged to take urgent action. Nasty old cynics might conclude that there are one or two things slightly more urgent on the NHS agenda.

As a writer in the *New York Times* stated some years ago: "A reason for the medical campaign against obesity may have to do with a tendency to medicalise behaviour we do not approve of." *The Times* remarks, without any hint of disapproval, "Today, the prejudice against fat is total. Ann Widdecombe is mocked by the media not for her policies but her weight." Political correctness prescribes that our female politicians all be Stepford wives, which most of the New Labour MPs (Blair's Babes) managed with consummate ease.

The Imperial Cancer Research Fund says it was confident that about 30 per cent of all cancers were related to diet. "People should be eating plenty of fruit and vegetables every day. Unfortunately, a good diet will not make up for other bad habits like drinking excessively and smoking." It said that eating five portions of fruit and vegetables a day, recommended by the Department of Health, should be seen as a minimum. This all goes back to the infamous 1981 book by Doll and Peto in which they made such claims on the basis of a cavalier disregard of the most important factor of all, age, of which more later.

The crescendo in the junk food campaign continued and in November 2003 the Government's new Food Standards Agency issued its report on "junk food". The establishment media quickly fell into line and published horror stories in line with the officially sponsored scare. The "evidence" came from one Gerald Hastings, a man who honed his propaganda skills at the Tobacco Control Research Centre, and his colleagues at the University of Strathclyde. In fact, there was no scientific evidence at all, just a "judgement".

A genuine Hamburger, the food that is always pictured to illustrate diatribes on junk food, is a highly nutritious item, though some of the commercial reproductions of this traditional delicacy might fall short of the ideal. Children have always resisted vegetables; well, from personal knowledge, they did half a century ago. There is no such thing as junk food; there are just balanced diets and unbalanced ones. There **is**, however, junk science and this is it.

One factor they always ignore is central heating. Modern children have not experienced waking up with ice on the inside of the bedroom window, or trudged through the snow on a long walk to school. They have never had to generate body heat by shivering.

Cholesterol

Most of the topics in this chapter have been dealt with in some brevity, with just a few samples of the items that appear in the media. Cholesterol is worth a closer look, as it provides a classical case of one erroneous scientific paper leading to widespread irrational behaviour supported by government regulation and scare campaigns. First, let us have a look at the establishment view, from *The Times*, Thursday March 29, 2001:

> **Medical Briefing**
> **Know your cholesterol**
> DR THOMAS STUTTAFORD
>
> *This week Sir Steven Redgrave presented to the press the new team he is training. His assorted crew of media figures includes Edwina Currie, Gloria*

Hunniford, Henry Cooper, Jack Charlton, Vanessa Feltz and record producer Peter Waterman. These celebrities have only one thing in common, other than their margarine-yellow T-shirts. They have all agreed to have their cholesterol levels measured and regularly monitored.

Sir Steven is going to be in charge of his team's fat intake and morale. He is to make certain that they stick to Flora pro.activ margarine and don't feel tempted to cheat on their fat intake by putting lashings of butter on their morning toast. The purpose of the campaign is to raise awareness of a raised blood level of low-density cholesterol (LDL) as one of the contributory causes of heart disease. Sir Steven will support the campaign by appearing in a series of television commercials — his first venture in his post-Olympic life.

Flora pro.activ was launched six months ago. In it, the Flora margarine is enriched with plants' sterols. Recent research has shown that raised cholesterol is no longer thought to be as important by the general public as it was a few years ago. Eighty per cent of adults in the UK still don't know their cholesterol levels, and even fewer are aware of the difference between the cardioprotective, high-density good cholesterol (HDL) and the dangerous, arterial-damaging low-density lipoprotein (LDL).

Sir Steven was aware of this disparity, but it seemed obvious as he chatted to his crew that his first task would have to be to teach them that it was a raised LDL, rather than a high total cholesterol, that was the sinister warning of choppy water ahead in life's race.

Sir Steven generously discussed his own health and blood fat levels with journalists over a low-fat, fruit-rich breakfast. Before taking up flora pro.activ, Sir Steven's cholesterol was high at 6.6 (the desired level is 5.2) but more significantly his pernicious LDL blood level, at 4.67, was very much higher than he could afford to accept with equanimity.

Sir Steven shouldn't have been too surprised. A raised LDL and overall cholesterol is usually found in diabetic patients, and he has had insulin-dependent diabetes for four years. Fortunately, after making no changes to his diet or his exercise regimen, other than swapping butter for Flora pro.activ margarine, his overall cholesterol has fallen to 5.5 and his LDL to 3.79. The LDL is just within acceptable limits.

Sir Steven said, however, that he had been surprised as he thought that raised cholesterol levels affected only "older, stressed businessmen types". He was wrong. Apart from his diabetes, which is often associated with raised blood fats, his highly competitive personality is just as likely to be type A as that of the competitive, ambitious banker. There is no difference between the financier collecting gold in vaults and athletes' gold around the *neck. The ideal exercise needed to maintain a healthy heart is regular steady exercise, daily if possible.*

A 10 per cent reduction in serum total cholesterol in 40-year-old males will reduce the risk of coronary heart disease by 50 per cent. It is claimed that changing to Flora pro.activ reduces the low- density lipoprotein by an average of 10 to 15 per cent in three weeks. Therefore, people who disregard their cholesterol levels do so at their own peril. They should insist on having LDL as well as total cholesterol measured annually as it increases with age and other factors.

One of the team, Vanessa Feltz, despite her recent psychological traumas in Celebrity Big Brother, *had a commendably low total cholesterol of 4.0, even before changing from saturated fats to Flora. Her level reflects her lifestyle. She has lost six stone, has a mixed diet with the approved daily ration of fruit and vegetables, takes regular exercise and doesn't smoke. She was surprised that the trials and tribulations of* Celebrity Big Brother *had not affected her blood results. As Sir Steven explained, though, personality and approach are some of the factors that make everyone's cholesterol different.*

A tendency to have high cholesterol levels has a strong genetic link. It was therefore interesting that Peter Waterman's immediate forebears all died before they were 52. Despite this handicap, his cholesterol was similar to that of the younger women and lower than that of Vanessa Feltz — in fact, it was so low that it couldn't be measured. Waterman had, however, been following a strict diet for more than three years.

Somewhere in the UK, someone dies of coronary heart disease every two minutes; it is still the primary cause of death in 25 per cent of all fatalities in England and Wales, and overwhelmingly the most common cause of premature death. In 40 per cent of these cases the people involved were unaware that they had anything the matter with their coronary arteries.

A good start in reducing this mortality would be to take whatever measures are necessary to reduce the LDL cholesterol level. Diet is the first; if this doesn't work, the wonder drugs, the statins, may be necessary.

This article, by one regarded by many as the doyen of medical journalists, is typical of the genre. There is a narrow line between straight medical reporting and snake oil salesmanship and this piece is the wrong side of it. The theory is the orthodox view, but the naked promotion of a particular product by means of scare tactics is, to say the least, ethically dubious. Let us look at the scientific reality.

The Cholesterol Myths by Dr Uffe Ravnskov is a remarkable book (see Bibliography). The author, a medical practitioner, has done more than just explode a family of well-entrenched myths; he has demonstrated just how the establishment maintains an orthodoxy in defiance of overwhelming contrary evidence. It does so, of course, by simply ignoring any facts that are inconvenient; *suppressio veri suggestio falsi*.

Ravnskov takes nine myths, which are:

> **High fat foods cause heart disease.**
> **High cholesterol causes heart disease.**
> **High-fat foods raise blood cholesterol.**
> **Cholesterol blocks arteries.**
> **Animal studies prove the heart-diet idea.**
> **Lowering your cholesterol will lengthen your life.**
> **Polyunsaturated oils are good for you.**
> **The cholesterol campaign is based on good science.**
> **All scientists support the diet-heart idea.**

He then looks at **all** the evidence, not just the papers favoured by the establishment, and disposes of the myths one by one. It is a scientific *tour de force*, for which he will, no doubt, be dismissed as a crank. It says much of the state of the modern world when those who adhere to the scientific method are cranks, while those who flout it win Nobel prizes.

The sheer brass neck with which authors select their data is truly astonishing. The very paper that started off the whole farrago in 1953 produced a smooth graph passing through data points for a small number of countries. Ravnskov, however, demonstrates that if you add the rest of the data, **which were available at the time**, the scatter diagram is all over the place. He cites several cases where the summary of a paper is at variance with its contents. Subsequent authors, of course, only look at the summary or, more often, an account of it by someone else.

Rather than reproduce the whole of Ravnkov's analysis and comparison, I have reproduced here the graph by Ancel Keys that started off the whole cholesterol business. I have, however, made certain alterations, which are:

1. Removal of the fitted curve and country labels
2. Addition of the data from the countries that Keys omitted
3. Removal of data from one country (Japan)

The last of these might seem dubious and needs some explanation. The human eye works very much like the mathematical process of least squares when looking for trends. It is one of the basic principles of *chartmanship* that a point near the origin of a graph gives a powerful impression of a strong relationship, even if the rest of the points are completely scattered. Japan happens to exhibit very low values for both the variables plotted and exerts such a pull. So here is the result, a plot of deaths from Coronary Heart Disease against fat consumption in various countries.

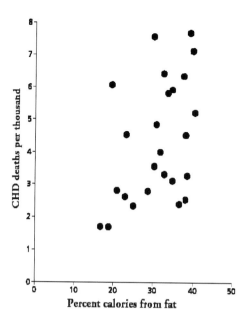

Figure 12.1 CHD v fat consumption for various countries

Now some people might feel confident that they could fit a smooth curve to these data, but few physical scientists would be tempted to do so. There are also a number of other points to be taken into consideration before making claims on such a basis. Above all there is our oft-repeated slogan **correlation is not causation**. In fact Ravnskov quotes evidence that CHD deaths follow a curve of sales of televisions sets closer than fat consumption, which stays relatively constant. There is an excellent correlation between CHD deaths and the local rate of tax in Sweden. In addition, however, there is also the question of accuracy of diagnosis. For example, in *Sorry (Chapter 13)* it is observed:

> *In fact, heart failure appears on death certificates far more often than is justified. In Britain it helps doctors to avoid the trauma of having to deal with the Coroner. The same constraints do no apply in some other countries; so we have a whole industry set up to explain why heart disease is more prevalent in Britain than in France, when the most likely explanation is the whim of the doctor signing the death certificate.*

We have already noted that Ravnskov quotes evidence that about half the death certificates citing CHD are wrong, and another study suggests that American doctors are 33% more likely to diagnose CHD than British ones and 50% more than Norwegians. The Japanese are strangely reluctant to diagnose heart disease (presumably for some cultural reason) and they don't eat much fat, which is why they exert so much influence on the curve drawing by plonking a point right by the origin.

Two papers giving the results of trials were published in the same journal. The one whose results did not support the orthodoxy received 15 citations over the next four years. The one favouring the orthodoxy, however, received 612 citations in the same period.

These are just some of the many methods used to prop up the myths, but we have seen them all elsewhere to maintain other establishment myths (the low salt diet, global warming, passive smoking etc.) Many of them have provided the foundation for huge industries, the cholesterol one being worth billions of dollars. They enable academics to establish reputations, large departments and win prizes. They enable medical practitioners to go through the motions without having to exercise too many brain cells. The sheer weight of interest in suppressing the truth is awesome. Thanks be that there are still a few small boys who are prepared to point out that the emperor has no clothes.

Just in case the reader is not convinced of the seriousness of the train of consequences that can arise from one bit of bad science, this is what the British Medical Journal told its readers half a century later in 2003.

> From April of next year, the salaries of many of BMJ readers will depend in part on serum cholesterol levels as documented in the new GMS contract. Attaining a total cholesterol level of <5 mmol/l in up to 60% of patients with coronary heart disease, diabetes and stroke accounts for 27 quality points.
>
> Small variations in serum cholesterol for a practice population may therefore have a big impact on income since achieving cholesterol targets in 2004/5 equates to a total of just over £2000 per average practice. We suggest that prudent practitioners will ask their patients to take their statin at night and will base their annual cholesterol check on a morning blood sample. This may or may not lead to improvements in patients' cardiovascular health but it should predictably lead to improvements in their doctors' bank balance!

Fat

Associated with cholesterol in the public mind as well as that of the medical establishment is that dread word FAT. Here is a piece from Canada by Brad Evenson of the *National Post*:

Tempting fat

For decades, healthy eating's mantra has been: Fat is bad. But despite cutting back, many Canadians remain overweight. Are we looking at what we eat the wrong way?

When Professor Stephen Cunnane's fourth-year nutrition class at the University of Toronto meets tomorrow, the students will debate a question most North Americans thought was dead 50 years ago: "Does dietary fat lead to obesity?"

Want to bet a Diet Coke on who wins?

Of all the dietary dogma that health advocates have preached since the Second World War, the precept most people can recite without strain is: Eat less fat, live longer. The very concept of healthy eating has become synonymous with eating less fat. McDonald's fries? Suicide. Fried eggs? Heart attack on a plate. During the past 30 years, the North American food industry has delivered more than 15,000 reduced-fat foods to supermarkets, from diet potato chips to low-fat salad dressings. Politicians, scientists and the media have all joined the chorus.

So your Diet Coke would appear safe.

But there is a discordant note. Science does not support this less-fat-is-good message. Despite hundreds of millions of dollars in research, no one has ever proved eating less dietary fat will extend a person's life by a day. In fact, there are good reasons to believe high-carbohydrate diets may be even worse than high-fat diets.

In a powerful article in the journal Science, writer Gary Taubes laid out the groundwork for a major shift in public thought about dietary fat.

Since the early 1970s, Americans' average fat intake has dropped from over 40% of total calories to 34%; average serum cholesterol levels have dropped as well. But no compelling evidence suggests these decreases have improved health or longevity. "Meanwhile, obesity in America, which remained constant from the early 1960s through 1980, has surged upward since then – from 14% of the population to over 22%," writes Taubes, who spent a year and interviewed over 150 scientists for the article.

In fact, many scientists in the United States and Canada say the evidence that fat is not particularly harmful has been covered up. One senior Harvard University epidemiologist branded it "scandalous."

The idea that dietary fat is harmful rests on the fact that saturated fat, the hard fat found in meat, can raise blood cholesterol levels. In turn, cholesterol can clog arteries, which raises the risk of coronary artery disease, which can cause a heart attack and death.

As Taubes points out, each link in this chain has been proven, but no one has ever scientifically demonstrated the whole chain, from steak to slab so to speak. In fact, numerous studies, including the Nurses Health Study and two follow-up studies, which spent 10 years compiling data on the diet and health of nearly 300,000 Americans, found no evidence to suggest dietary fat has any relation to heart disease risk.

A 10-year review of heart disease published in the New England Journal of Medicine in 1998 supported this finding when it concluded death rates are declining not because of lower-fat diets, but because doctors are treating heart disease with greater success. In fact, more people are having heart attacks, but fewer are dying from them. Doctors in Canada now perform four times more medical procedures for heart disease than they did 20 years ago; clearly, the disease is not withering away on a diet of fat-free Thousand Islands dressing.

Although the anti-fat movement began in the 1960s, it took off in 1977 when a U.S. congressional committee led by senator George McGovern suggested Americans should reduce their fat intake to 30% of total calories, with only 10% from saturated (hard) fat. That report was influenced by a Harvard School of Public Health nutritionist, Mark Hegsted, a zealot on the merits of reducing fat intake whose opinion was considered extreme and unfounded. Despite the protests of prominent scientists, the report's central idea became U.S. policy: Eat less fat, live longer. Indeed, Canada's Food Guide still advises, "Choose low fat foods more often," and recommends not consuming more than 30% of calories from fat. If Canadians are following this advice, why are close to 50% of us overweight?

"I think people have looked for at least the past half-century for simple ways to solve complex health problems," says Cunnane. "And so it's intrinsically sensible, empirically at least, that one would link dietary fat to fatness – to body fat. It seems plausible on the surface. I think a lot of scientists have supported that, and obviously the food industry has taken a greater and greater interest in the past half-century in preparing foods, I guess, according to consumer demand. So I wouldn't blame anyone specifically."

The confusion over what to eat has not been made any easier by the plethora of diet books, each espousing an extreme course of action. They range from diets high in carbohydrates but low in fat, such as Dr. Dean Ornish's Program for Reversing Heart Disease, to Dr. Robert Atkins' New Diet Revolution, which claims that cutting out carbohydrates and adding protein will cause the pounds to melt away. What these books share, however, is the general advice that whatever you do, cutting out dietary fat is the first step.

However, the reason so many North Americans are obese, says Cunnane, is not dietary fat intake but total intake of calories, combined with a lack of physical activity to burn them off. For example, many young patients with severe epilepsy are fed a therapeutic diet in which 80% of calories come from fat, mostly dairy fat. "There are probably 5,000 kids on the diet in North America, and they're not fat," he says. "They're losing weight. So extremely high fat does not necessarily mean that people will get fat."

Wider evidence of this phenomenon can be found in southern Europe, where rates of heart disease have declined steadily even as the rate of meat consumption has climbed. The residents of France, Italy and Greece consume a large proportion of their diet as fat, but they eat smaller amounts than North Americans, who tend to consume food in quantities that foreigners find appalling, and precious little of it in fruit or vegetable form.

As University of Cambridge epidemiologist John Powles puts it, the anti-fat movement was founded on the Puritan notion that "something bad had to have an evil cause, and you got a heart attack because you did something wrong, which was eating too much of a bad thing, rather than not having enough of a good thing."

The result of this aversion to dietary fat is still unclear, but many scientists suspect it may cause harm. Fat serves many vital purposes; the brain is 50% to 70% fat. Cell membranes are mostly fat. And there is some concern that children are no longer getting enough fat in their diets for optimal brain development.

Fats also take myriad forms, ranging from saturated fats in animal products to unsaturated fats in olive oil, avocados, nuts and other nutritious foods. Indeed, some fat, most notably Omega-3 fatty acids -- found in fish and some vegetables – is believed by many scientists to have powerful health properties.

"They lower triglycerides, they reduce platelet aggregation [blood clots], they reduce cardiac arrhythmia, which is the leading cause of sudden death," says Cunnane, noting one major study found that eating Omega-3 fatty acids reduces cancer risk. Indeed, some authorities believe the lack of Omega-3 fats may be an underlying cause of many slow-developing psychiatric illnesses. "The evidence is not strong, but I think people need to be alerted to this risk."

None of this means a steady diet of cheeseburgers and Survivor reruns will make you healthier. However, it does debunk the notion that fat alone greases the road to heart disease.

"Enjoy the taste of fat," advises Cunnane. "If you like chocolate, get good chocolate. Pay a little bit more, eat a bit less, and you'll be satisfied. Buy the best ice cream you can afford. Enjoy it, and hopefully you will appreciate that you don't have to eat the whole barrel tonight. Whereas with the lower-fat varieties, you're not getting that mouth-feel and flavour and taste. And I think that's where the Europeans are ahead of us here in North America, as far as their long-term risk of fat intake."

"So enjoy fat. Enjoy exercise."
***

CONSIDER A STEAK ...:

"... to be precise, a porterhouse, select cut, with a half-centimetre layer of fat, the nutritional constituents of which can be found in the Nutrient Database for Standard Reference at the U.S. Department of Agriculture Web site.

After broiling, this porterhouse reduces to a serving of almost equal parts fat and protein. Fifty-one percent of the fat is mono-unsaturated, of which virtually all (90%) is oleic acid, the same healthy fat that's in olive oil. Saturated fat constitutes 45% of the total fat, but a third of that is stearic acid, which is, at the very least, harmless. The remaining 4% of the fat is poly-unsaturated, which also improves cholesterol levels.

In sum, well over half -- and perhaps as much as 70% -- of the fat content of a porterhouse will improve cholesterol levels compared to what they would be if bread, potatoes or pasta were consumed instead. The remaining 30% will raise LDL [bad cholesterol] but will also raise HDL [good cholesterol].

"All of this suggests that eating a porterhouse steak rather than carbohydrates might actually improve heart disease risk, although no nutritional authority who hasn't written a high-fat diet book will say this publicly."

Gary Taubes, Science

Although the above articles effectively explode the fat myth, they also, unfortunately, maintain several others.

Of course, the news is not always bad. Doctors at Great Ormond Street Hospital tested whether a high-fat, low carbohydrate regime known as a ketogenic diet could have more of an impact than taking drugs to control epilepsy. Of the 14 children who had been on the diet for at least three months, more than half saw a 50% reduction of seizures. In four cases, the seizures were reduced by 75%.

Vitamins

The banner headline that takes up most of the front page of the *Daily Mail* (June 15th 2001) is **Vitamin C cancer fear**. It is all based on test tube experiments at the University of Pennsylvania, which suggest that the substance can cause damage to DNA. Readers of *Sorry, wrong number!* will recognise the *concentration fallacy* and the *missing link* among the nonsenses in this scare. Mind you, the evidence that large doses of the vitamin do any good is equally suspect.

This from BBC Scotland, December 2001

Pregnant women could prevent their children developing asthma and other allergies by eating food which is rich in vitamin E, new research has suggested.

Researchers at Aberdeen University discovered that children whose mothers had a higher intake of the vitamin in their diet were less sensitive to common allergens like pollen and dust mites.

As no numbers are given, it is not possible to comment further.

Then some articles send mixed signals Reuters, November 2001:

University of Washington researchers concluded in one study that antioxidant vitamins such as C and E seem to the hinder the ability of two types of cholesterol drugs -- statins and niacin -- to reduce the risk of a heart attack or chest pain.

When patients avoid the antioxidant pills, the combination of the drugs simvastatin (sold under the brand name Zocor by Merck and Company Inc.) and niacin, which is actually Vitamin B-3, reduced the risk of heart attack for chest pain by 70 percent, they concluded.

In the other study, researchers at the University of California San Diego found that a combination of folic acid and vitamins B-12 and B-6 seemed to keep once-clogged heart arteries open after doctors enlarged them with a procedure known as angioplasty.

A team led by Dr. Guido Schnyder said when the vitamins, which cost pennies a day, were given after angioplasty to 105 patients, the chance the reopened blood vessel would narrow again declined by 48 percent, compared with the risk for the 100 volunteers who received placebos.

Tomatoes

A nice dilemma for the food freaks. Tomatoes have been produced that have increased levels of anti-oxidant compounds called flavonols. According to *The Times* these are "known" to lower the risk of heart disease, inflammation, cellular ageing and several cancers. Unfortunately, the wonder tomatoes are produced by Genetic Modification. Will the gullible masses be like the proverbial donkey, who starved to death because he was between two bales of hay and could not decide which to choose?

For tomatoes have become a major fetish among epidemiologists. For example, Dr. Edward Giovannucci of Harvard University states that eating tomatoes is an effective way to reduce the risk of prostate cancer. His studies show that 10 servings of tomato rich foods per week reduced the risk by 45% and 4 to 7 servings reduced the risk by 20%. The tomato, we are told, is rich in *lycopene,* which gives it the distinctive red color. Lycopene is a powerful antioxidant, more potent than *beta-carotene.* Therefore the lycopene molecule "may" act to block the initiation of the cancerous process.

Fish

A BBC text headline in January 2001 dutifully reported the latest outcome from the *data dredge* known as the Harvard Nurses' Health Study. It appears that women who regularly eat fish four times a week had a 27% smaller chance of having a stroke. All the junk characteristics that we have come to know and love are there – the *Trojan Number* of 80,000 in the study, though only 0.7% of them had strokes, reliance on self-reporting, and a ludicrously insignificant *relative risk*. What we are not told is how many women ate fish four times a week. Do you know any? If you do, did they have a minnow or a shark?

The truly amazing thing with epidemiologists, however, that puts them beyond us ordinary mortals, is that on such flimsy evidence that are not only able to identify fish as the saviour, but are able to home in with unerring accuracy on *n 3 polyunsaturated fatty acids*. Amazing Holmes! Commonplace Watson.

300,000,000,000 to 1 is the dilution of the dreaded PCBs in farmed salmon that caused the first big food scare of 2001 (*The Times*, and everywhere else, January 4th). This is the sort of number that is difficult for the ordinary human to comprehend. If you were able to count the molecules in a salmon once a second, you would find a PCB once every ten thousand years. The BBC described this concentration as "high levels" of man-made toxins. What dilution would it require to be low level, for heaven's sake? The author of this scare, one Miriam Jacobs of Surrey University, was able to produce it because of advances in instrumentation, on this occasion under the auspices of the EPA (where else?) in Mississippi. Half a millennium ago, in the early beginnings of the rational era, which has recently come to an end, Paracelsus stated that poison was in the dose. In the new era such truisms have been forgotten. Even the most virulent toxin known to man (Botulism toxin A) would be safe at this concentration in the human body. You could tolerate the dreaded sodium cyanide at many millions of times the concentration. Nevertheless, the World Hysteria Organisation (WHO) has declared that these are the orders of magnitude that mark the limit of safety.

Salmon farming is a damned nuisance. Its products are ragged fatty abortions, which contaminate the wild variety with lice, disease and genetic corruption. It is not, however, going to kill anybody. PCBs, dioxins and furans, which are notoriously found in all fish, have probably always been there. They are the natural products of combustion, and nature invented fire long before man.

The whole salmon scare erupted again in January 2004, this time promoted by American epidemiologists. It was all over the media. It makes one proud to be British that as a result salmon sales rose by about 20% the following week.

Coffee

Coffee does not cause breast cancer says the headline on the BBC text news. Not a very notable story, you might say, and the media agreed. It was put out by Reuters on December 23rd 2001, but nobody took it up. A 13-year-long study of 60,000

Swedish women found no link suggesting coffee would be a culprit "We found no association between self-reported coffee, black tea, and caffeine consumption and subsequent breast cancer incidence," said the research report made at the Karolinska Institute medical university, most famous for choosing the annual winner of the Nobel prize for medicine. In contrast the original scare story 20 years before had wide coverage.

Here is another "good news" coffee story that made it into the papers:

> (Boston Herald Jan 99) Maybe you should skip the bran muffin and have an extra cup of coffee instead. Now that it has been shown that eating a high-fiber diet does not protect against colon cancer, some are looking to java as a way to prevent the deadly disease. Dr. Edward Giovannucci of the Harvard School of Public Health published a study last year suggesting that the risk of colorectal cancer drops 24 percent among those who drink four or more cups of coffee a day.

On the whole, however, the press prefers scares to breakthroughs and coffee is a frequent target. Its ubiquity ensures press coverage and allows "results" to be generated from the cheapest type of subjective, post-hoc questionnaire. *The American Journal of Clinical Nutrition*, October 2001:

> Nutrition, lifestyle, and genetics may all contribute to the decrease in bone mineral density (BMD) that comes with aging and leads to osteoporosis, a major cause of fractures in the elderly. Previous research implicated caffeine in increased risk for hip fracture and poor calcium retention. As part of a larger long-term study of osteoporosis, Rapuri et al. compared the BMD of women in high and low categories of caffeine consumption to examine the interaction between caffeine intake, genetic type, and osteoporosis. They found that women with high caffeine intakes had significantly higher rates of bone loss at the spine, and that women who were homozygous for a mutation in the vitamin D receptor (VDR) gene were at greater risk for caffeine-related bone loss.

> The 96 women, averaging 71 years old were not taking any calcium or Vitamin D supplements. Using 7-day food diaries the researchers divided them into low (less than 300 mg/day) or high (greater than 300 mg/day) caffeine intake levels. BMD at the spine, hip, and three other sites was measured, and each subject's VDR genotype was determined. Calculation of the percent change in BMD during the 3-year longitudinal study showed that a caffeine intake of more than 300 mg/day was associated with a higher rate of bone loss at most of the skeletal sites in the spine, although the difference was only significant in subjects carrying the homozygous tt genotype of VDR. Women in the high caffeine category with the tt genotype lost bone density over 3years, compared with no change in bone density the tt women in the low caffeine group.

Though the number of women with the tt genotype was relatively small (6 in the low caffeine group and 5 in the high caffeine group), these findings identify caffeine as a dietary factor, which can alter one's genetic predisposition toward osteoporosis. An editorial by Massey stresses that moderate caffeine ingestion – less than 16 ounces of brewed coffee per day or 32 ounces of brewed tea – is not associated with increased bone loss. Until it is practical to determine each person's VDR genotype, physicians should recommend both adequate dietary calcium and moderate caffeine consumption for their elderly patients.

The Times September 2001

Coffee is linked to heart disease

FROM HELEN RUMBELOW IN STOCKHOLM
JUST one cup of coffee a day is enough to increase the risk of heart disease — and the first cup of the day is the most dangerous, according to researchers at the European Society of Cardiology in Stockholm.

The study is the first to measure the effect of coffee on arteries, and found that one cup hardened the blood vessels for at least two hours, raising blood pressure and putting the heart under strain.

Charalambos Vlachopoulos, who led the study at the Henry Dunant Hospital in Athens, said that the results were so striking that the elderly and people with high blood pressure should consider switching to a decaffeinated coffee or stop drinking it.

The findings showed that the first cup had the most significant effect because caffeine levels in the blood had dropped during the night. The second and third cups caused only marginally worse hardening of the arteries.

Reuters Health, Nov 22, 2001

Drinking more than two cups of coffee daily may boost estrogen levels in women and could exacerbate conditions such as endometriosis and breast pain, study findings suggest.

According to the researchers, women who drank the most coffee had higher levels of estradiol, a naturally occurring form of estrogen, during the early follicular phase, or days 1 to 5 of the menstrual cycle.

"Higher estrogen levels would not be beneficial for women who for example have endometriosis, breast pain and family histories of breast or ovarian cancer, especially arising premenopausally," the study's lead author, Dr. Daniel W. Cramer from Brigham and Women's Hospital in Boston, Massachusetts, told Reuters Health.

"It is my personal advice that such women should be discouraged from consuming more than two cups of coffee per day," Cramer said.

The study included nearly 500 women aged 36 to 45 who were not pregnant, breast-feeding or taking hormones. All women answered questions about their diets, smoking habits, height and weight. Researchers measured the women's hormone levels during days 1 to 5 of their menstrual cycle.

Women who consumed the most cholesterol and alcohol, and those who consumed more than one cup of coffee a day had significantly higher levels of estrogen during the early follicular phase of their menstrual cycle, according to the report in the October issue of Fertility and Sterility.

In fact, caffeine intake from all sources was linked with higher estrogen levels regardless of age, body mass index (BMI), caloric intake, smoking, and alcohol and cholesterol intake. Women who consumed at least 500 milligrams of caffeine daily, the equivalent of four or five cups of coffee, had nearly 70% more estrogen during the early follicular phase than women consuming no more than 100 mg of caffeine daily, or less than one cup of coffee.

Women aged 40 and older and those who smoked had higher levels of follicle stimulating hormone (FSH), which reflects the number of eggs remaining in a woman's ovaries. FSH tends to increase with age, and high levels of the hormone correspond with fewer eggs. Therefore, the observation that smokers have higher FSH levels suggests that their ovaries are "older" than their chronological age, Cramer explained.

"Our study provides a basis for believing that coffee consumption increases estradiol levels," Cramer said. "While these effects are modest with one or two cups, they are more evident at higher levels of consumption."

According to a Readers Digest health book coffee that has been percolated or stewed (not instant coffee) may increase cholesterol level, in the blood.

High coffee intake can cause stillbirth

Nigel (thousands to die) Hawkes of *The Times* found a delectable *Trojan Number* to back up this scary headline. The BBC made do with **Coffee pregnancy warning.** The number was 18,478, but how many actually contributed to the headline? The answer is just **eleven**. The original paper from Denmark derives a relative risk of 3.0 from this number. On the face of it, in view of our discussion of *relative risk*, we should accept this as significant, but just have a look at the 95% confidence interval, which is 1.5 to 5.9. This is typical of what happens when you try to make deductions from tiny numbers. A range this large at such an undemanding level of significance is an indicator of nonsense.

The paper is a classic in many ways. It is a *data dredge*, but one that mainly looks at the usual suspects – coffee, alcohol and tobacco. What "researchers" choose to ignore when they do this is the fact these substances are all notable stress relievers and their excessive use is a symptom rather than a cause. Most of us like coffee, but more than eight cups a day? This was the intake for which the causality was claimed.

Another classical feature of the paper is that it goes on to perform all sorts of adjustments. It is a particular delight that, after all the adjustments, the confidence interval becomes 1.0 to 4.7; again it includes unity, which means no correlation at all. Here is another small selection of headlines:

Scientist finds decaffeinated coffee doubles chance of rheumatoid arthritis
Study finds coffee may help battle colon cancer
Scientists cool on coffee cancer theory
Caffeine intake increases the rate of bone loss in elderly women
Coffee drinking associated with reduced risk of diabetes

Chocolate

While coffee gets a mixed, though mainly hostile, reception from the establishment, chocolate seems to lead a charmed life.

A Penn State-led study has found that a diet high in flavonoid-rich cocoa powder and dark chocolate had favorable effects on LDL ("bad" cholesterol) when compared with a diet that limited or excluded other flavonoid sources such as tea, coffee, wine, onions, apples, beans, soybeans, and orange and grape juices.

Dr. Penny Kris-Etherton, Penn State distinguished professor of nutrition and leader of the study, says, "Cocoa and chocolate are 'fun food' and I think these results show that they can contribute to a healthy diet – especially if they are used in forms that don't include large amounts of fat and sugar. However, cocoa and chocolate shouldn't be considered significant sources of flavonoids in the same category with fruits and vegetables which also have fiber, vitamins and minerals."

Reuters, September 2001

Good news for chocoholics. The treat favored by millions not only tastes delicious but is healthy for you, American researchers said on Monday. Chocolate contains compounds called flavonoids that can help maintain a healthy heart and good circulation and reduce blood clotting -- which can cause heart attacks and strokes. "More and more, we are finding evidence that consumption of chocolate that is rich in flavonoids can have positive cardiovascular effects," Carl Keen, a nutritionist at the University of California, Davis, told a science conference. "We not only have observed an increase in antioxidant capacity after chocolate consumption, but also modulation of certain compounds which affect blood vessels."

Antioxidants are substances that help reduce the damage of cancer-causing charged particles in the body. Fruits, vegetables, nuts and whole grains are high in antioxidant vitamins such as C and E.

Not all chocolate created equal

Flavonoids in chocolate are derived from cocoa, which is rich in the compounds. Research has shown that a small bar of dark chocolate contains as many flavonoids as six apples, 4.5 cups of tea, 28 glasses of white wine and two glasses of red.

But Dr. Harold Schmitz said there were variations in the levels of flavonoids in chocolate and cocoa products depending on the production process, in which many flavonoids are destroyed. "All chocolates are not created equal in regards to flavonoid content," Schmitz, **a scientist with confectionery maker Mars Inc**, told a news conference.

Flavonoids are **thought** to reduce the risk of cardiovascular disease, the number one killer in many industrialized countries, by reducing platelet aggregation -- when blood platelets combine into a sticky mass and form clots.

Keen and his colleagues measured the impact of chocolate on platelets in the blood in **25** volunteers. They presented their findings to the British Association for the Advancement of Science conference in Glasgow. The researchers collected blood samples from volunteers who ate 25 grams (0.9 ounces) of chocolate with a high flavonoid content and other volunteers who ate bread. They took blood samples from both groups two and six hours after they ate the chocolate and bread to measure their platelet activation.

Volunteers who consumed the chocolate had lower levels of platelet activity, which would reduce the probability of having a blood clot. The scientists found no change in the group that ate the bread. Keen said the results of the study support earlier research showing that cocoa acts like low-dose aspirin which helps to reduce blood clotting. But he warned that eating chocolate should not be substituted for taking low dose aspirin because they work through different mechanism in the body.
"These results lead us to believe that chocolate may contribute to a healthy, well-balanced diet," Keen added.

Up to 300 scientists are presenting research on subjects ranging from genetics and microbiology to global warming and organic farming during the five-day conference.

Another report managed to tell the same story but had the wit to link it to a then fashionable health scare:

A BAR of chocolate before a long-haul flight may help to protect against "economy-class syndrome", according to American scientists.

Chocolate is one of the richest dietary sources of chemicals that control a key clotting agent in the blood and is likely to reduce the risk of deep-vein thrombosis.

A study at the University of California-Davis showed that a mug of cocoa or a bar of chocolate have a similar beneficial effect on the blood as a low dose of aspirin, which doctors already recommend to patients at risk of developing the disease.

Within six hours of drinking the cocoa, volunteers had much lower levels of clot-promoting proteins in their bloodstreams. An analysis of samples showed that their blood took longer to clot than those in a control group. Eating chocolate produced similar results.

"This is a reduction in the probability that people will have a blood clot, or some sort of thrombosis," said Carl Keen, Professor of Nutrition and Internal Medicine, who led the research. He suggested that chocolate might make a difference to air passengers' chances of developing a clot, although no specific tests have been done yet.

Tea

This beverage also leads a charmed life in epidemiological circles. Here are just a few recent headlines:

Tea good for the bones
Tea may protect against Parkinson's
Tea prevents heart attacks
Lemon tea fights skin cancer

In Britain this is all largely due to the assiduous placing of stories by the Tea Council, but the phenomenon is worldwide.

Weedkillers

Daily Telegraph May 6, 2000

EXPOSURE to chemical pesticides and weedkillers in the home and garden may double the risk of developing Parkinson's disease.

Researchers who studied the lives of more than 1,000 people said chemical sprays and pellets could damage brain nerve cells. Lorene Nelson and colleagues at the Stanford University School of Medicine in California questioned 496 people newly diagnosed with Parkinson's about their use of pesticides, weedkillers and fungicides.

The results were compared with answers from 541 people without the disease. People who had been exposed to insecticides were more than twice as likely to have developed Parkinson's than those with no exposure, the researchers found. Pesticide exposure in the home was associated with the greatest risk. Use of weedkillers was also linked to Parkinson's, although exposure to insecticides in the open air and the use of fungicides were not found to be risk factors.

Dr Nelson said: "This study is the largest yet of newly diagnosed individuals with Parkinson's and it is the first to show a significant association between home pesticide use and the risk of developing the disease." The preliminary results, presented at the American Academy of Neurology's annual meeting in San Diego, California, support previous studies which have linked occupational exposure to pesticides with Parkinson's.

The muscle tremor and stiffness characteristic of Parkinson's is caused by damage to nerve cells in the basal ganglia. The scientists believe people exposed to chemicals that have a particular affinity for this region of the brain may have an increased risk of developing the condition. Dr Nelson said: "Certain chemicals in the environment may cause selective death of brain cells."

But other factors are probably also important, including an individual's genetic susceptibility, she said. Dr Nelson said more studies would have to be carried out before definite conclusions could be drawn: "No specific guidelines regarding avoidance of pesticides can be given at this time but, in general, this is an area of public health importance that needs to be pursued."

The symptoms of Parkinson's disease are thought to be caused by the loss of the neurotransmitter dopamine in the brain.

Soya

It was not a matter of whether but when the Great Food Scare of the Silly Season of 2000 would eruct. The fifteen minutes of fame scroll of honour went to two geniuses working for the FDA, Daniel George and Daniel Sheehan. **Soya linked to cancer and brain damage** yelled the front-page headline in the *Observer* (August 13). What a stroke of brilliance to pick on what is one of the most popular foods in the world! Of course, in the rational age, which finally came to an end some twenty years before, it would have been noticed that all the millions feeding on the stuff did not show any extra unusual symptoms at all. Anthony Barnet, Public Affairs Editor for the *Observer* should receive a special award for a sentence that epitomises the age of junk:

> *Although soy is thought to protect against breast cancer, some studies show that chemicals in Soya may increase the chances of breast cancer, which uses oestrogen type hormones for growth.*

In April 2001 the University of Alabama announced that **Soy cuts Alzheimer's risk**. In November 2001 it was announced that preliminary results of a University of Missouri study indicate compounds found in high soy-based diets **may** help provide protection against prostate cancer. The next month The University of Illinois "Cast doubt on soya for the menopause". These are just a few of the soy stories that hit the headlines in that year alone.

Which brings us to a thought from George Orwell's 1984:

> *Doublethink means the power of holding two contradictory beliefs in one's mind simultaneously, and accepting both of them.*

Common salt

Why ordinary table salt should be picked on as a cause of high blood pressure is something of a mystery. It might have arisen through some vague idea of osmotic pressure, but it rapidly became an established tenet of admonitory medicine, without the slightest iota of evidence. Considering it was once a substance so valued that Roman soldiers were partly paid in it (hence the word salary) this is a massive turnaround. Recently, however, a review of 56 clinical trials of hypertensive and normotensive individuals, concluded that this was nonsense. There is even evidence from a study of hypertensive men that a low sodium diet actually increases risk of heart attack. (Hypertension. 1995;25:1144-1152). The salt debate is one of the long running sagas of epidemiology, involving endless arguments over marginal statistics. For a full review by Gary Taubes see *Science*, August 14, 1998.

Of all the substances, Sodium Chloride is one of the most essential compounds for the existence of life on earth. It makes up about three percent of the mass of the sea. The trick by which animals were able to leave the sea was to carry it around inside them in the form of blood plasma. You need the chlorine to manufacture hydrochloric acid, which is the main component of the gastric juices. The sodium plays an essential role in the transmission of nerve impulses. Without salt in your diet you will die. You can get a sufficient dosage from a natural diet, as it is also essential to other life forms, but it adds a harmless piquancy to many dishes. Excess salt is readily excreted without ill effect. Of course, if you seriously overdose, you will also die.

For a classic case of the *virtual body count* based on a shadow without substance, it is hard to beat this one in October 2003:

> *Professor Graham MacGregor, head of cardiovascular medicine of St George's Hospital Medical School, said an immediate cut of 10 per cent in salt in the average diet would save 5,800 lives over the next year and is unhappy that this is not being forced upon manufacturers. 'The industry tells us that they can't cut salt levels immediately because the customers won't like the taste, but lots of studies show that such a reduction wouldn't be detectable. I find it astonishing that a train operator can be held accountable if he causes deaths in a rail crash but we don't hold the manufacturers responsible for these many thousands of preventable deaths because so much salt is hidden in processed food.'*

In fact, salt in Britain has a whole Single Issue Fanatic group of its own called CASH (Consensus on Salt and Health). Despite the fact that not a single study has ever produced any serious evidence connecting salt with disease or death, they trot out endless propaganda, including a National Salt Awareness day every January with presentations to Parliament. Government ministers obediently follow the script. Their evidence is based on *meta-analyses* that claim to establish a link between salt intake and blood pressure. Some of the studies invoked are based on as few as **19** patients. The evidence takes the form of a trend fitted to widely scattered points on a graph of blood pressure against excreted salt. Any engineering or physics student producing such graph would have his laboratory logbook thrown back at him. Even if this were true it would be a logical fallacy to deduce that salt causes disease. If, for example, high blood pressure were a symptom of a disorder and also a symptom of excess salt intake, that would not link salt to the disorder.

Because of the anti-salt campaign, many medical authorities have abandoned the age-old prescription of salt tablets for dehydration due to heat or exercise. Salt is excreted through perspiration (you can taste it in your sweat) and a deficiency results in the extremely painful condition known as cramp. Lack of salt causes a breakdown in the mechanism by which the nerves control the muscles and the muscle goes into a painful spasm. A salt tablet will often effect a cure.

Spinach

Ask almost anyone what food you should eat for more iron and the reply would almost certainly be "Spinach". In fact, spinach contains no more iron than most other legumes or brassicas. There is a story, probably apocryphal, that German scientists discovered that someone making the original assessment misplaced a decimal point and multiplied the figure by ten. Nevertheless, whatever the origin, the wartime propaganda in the US at a time when meat was short promoted the career of Popeye the Sailorman and put the myth into the worldwide human consciousness. Nothing to do with epidemiology, but it shows the longevity of a myth once it is successfully planted. The consumption of spinach increased by a third in America. Then as now, myths create industries.

Cranberry juice

This rather obscure dietary item also seems to have a charmed life among the epidemiologists, e.g:

> Researchers have found cranberry juice may combat heart disease by raising levels of "good" cholesterol and antioxidants. A US study suggests that drinking three glasses of cranberry juice a day could reduce heart disease risk by 40%. A group of **19** volunteers with high cholesterol were given between one and three glasses of juice a day over a period of three months. Scientists found that three servings appeared to increase levels of high density lipoprotein (HDL) cholesterol by an average of **10%.** HDL is known as "good" cholesterol because unlike "bad" low density lipoprotein it protects against heart disease. The increase corresponded to a reduction in heart disease risk of about 40%, based on known epidemiological data. At the same time the researchers found that the amount of antioxidants available to the body increased by up to 121% after two or three glasses of cranberry juice a day. Antioxidants mop up dangerous atomic particles called free radicals and are also known to reduce the risk of heart disease, as well as cancer. Professor Joe Vinson, from the University of Scranton in Pennsylvania, who led the research, said: "This study gives consumers another reason to consider drinking cranberry juice, which has more health benefits than previously believed." He now plans to test the effect of cranberry juice on volunteers with normal cholesterol levels.

Fibre

The epidemiologists and dieticians love this one. It has been claimed at various times to cure all ills. Here is a typical example of the research behind such claims, published in the *Archives of Internal Medicine* in September 2003.

First, let's look at what they did:

> **Methods** We examined the relationship between total and soluble dietary fiber intake and the risk of CHD and cardiovascular disease (CVD) in 9776 adults who participated in the National Health and Nutrition Examination Survey I Epidemiologic Follow-up Study and were free of CVD at baseline. A 24-hour dietary recall was conducted at the baseline examination, and nutrient intakes were calculated using Food Processor software. Incidence and mortality data for CHD and CVD were obtained from medical records and death certificates during follow-up.

Can this really mean what it appears to say? They took anecdotal evidence of diet just one day and used that as a basis for a 19-year follow up? But the best is yet to come:

> **Results** During an average of 19 years of follow-up, 1843 incident cases of CHD and 3762 incident cases of CVD were documented. Compared with the lowest quartile of dietary fiber intake (median, 5.9 g/d), participants in the highest quartile (median, 20.7 g/d) had an adjusted relative risk of 0.88 (95% confidence interval [CI], 0.74-1.04; P = .05 for trend) for CHD events and of 0.89 (95% CI, 0.80-0.99; P = .01 for trend) for CVD events. The relative risks for those in the highest (median, 5.9 g/d) compared with those in the lowest (median, 0.9 g/d) quartile of water-soluble dietary fiber intake were 0.85 (95% CI, 0.74-0.98; P = .004 for trend) for CHD events and 0.90 (95% CI, 0.82-0.99; P = .01 for trend) for CVD events.

Just look at those *relative risks*, and *confidence intervals*! This all leads to the glorious:

> **Conclusion** A higher intake of dietary fiber, particularly water-soluble fiber, reduces the risk of CHD.

What on earth is "$p = 0.004$ for trend" supposed to mean? Does it apply to all four points or just two? Either way almost any four random numbers will reveal an apparent significant trend. How do they calculate it? Quoting p for trend seems to be the new trend among junk epidemiologists. As the magic word "Tulane" would suggest, this is one for the annals of inanity.

Selenium

The *Daily Mail* for September 12th carried a full page article by one Dr John Briffa headlined **How many diseases can selenium beat?** According to the opening paragraph, this trace element shows great promise in the war against cancer, and **may** also help to combat conditions as diverse as infertility, dementia, low thyroid function and AIDS. It goes on – "On Christmas day 1996, a scientific study was published which demonstrated selenium's ability to halve deaths due to some cancers. Since then the focus of much scientific research, it is clear that selenium's health giving properties are nothing short of remarkable."

This actually came from a paper by Larry C. Clark of the University of Arizona, with full supporting cast of fifteen co-authors, in the *Journal of the American Medical Association*. It is the usual bunkum, based on marginal statistics (e.g. a *relative risk* of 0.63, which is unacceptable in real science) and a tiny population.

On the other hand, two years later another eructation of junk science showed that Italians who had high levels of selenium in their water supply had a quadrupled risk of malignant melanoma.

Radon

Radon is the heaviest of the noble (i.e. non-reactive) gases. It is formed by the disintegration of radium and uranium. The gas tends to collect in tiny concentrations in some houses, particularly those built on or of granite. Because of the low concentrations and the operation of radiation *hormesis*, it is almost certainly harmless, and this view is supported by a number of direct studies, such as one in Finland in 1996; but that does not deter the scaremongers, particularly the EPA. **Radon Link in 21,800 Deaths a Year** yelled the AP headline in 1998. Thus a gigantic and expensive scam was built up on the usual basis of the *Linear Extrapolation* or *Zero Threshold* Fallacy. Also in 1998, Michael Fumento, a leading polemicist in the common sense camp, published an article in the *Investors Business Daily* headlined **Time To Overthrow The Radonistas**, he continued:

> *Lions and tigers and BEIRs, oh my! Specifically, BEIR VI, which is the sixth report of the Board on the Effects of Ionizing Radiation.*
>
> *BEIR VI is the latest effort to bilk homeowners out of more than $10 billion in the jihad against household radon, a radioactive gas that probably harms no one at the household level. The report was issued in February by the National Research Council, an arm of the National Academy of Sciences, and was co-funded by the Environmental Protection Agency.......*
>
> *Yet even those who've studied the miners, such as Dr. Gino Saccomanno of St. Mary's Hospital in Grand Junction, Colo., question whether anything shy of massive radon exposure can kill.*
>
> *Saccomanno has studied uranium miner disease for 40 years, and has by far the largest miner database in the country. He hasn't found a single case of lung cancer among nonsmoking uranium miners who breathe in radon eight hours a day, five days a week. A homeowner would have to breathe in what the EPA considers "dangerous" levels of radon for 400 years to get that kind of exposure.*
>
> *"I hate to see the public get taken like this," an exasperated Saccomanno said.*

If you want to probe the whole history of the radon scare go to Fumento's personal web site. It is a sorry saga, but an expensive one.

Dioxins

Not a week goes by without the phrase *cancer causing dioxins* appearing somewhere in the media, often all over them. The term covers over 200 different compounds. There is no evidence that they are human carcinogens. Of course, if you smear them in outrageous concentrations on the bodies of pathetic rodents bred to be tumour-prone you get, wait for it, tumours. Dioxins occur naturally as the products of combustion, which led to a nice little sub-scare when millions of animals were being burnt as part of the epidemiological holocaust (see chapter 15).

The salmon scare above was one of the many that relied on minuscule concentrations of these substances. The likelihood is that they were always there, but we are only now able to detect them, like the hole in the ozone layer.

PCBs

Polychlorinated biphenyls have been valuable materials in modern technology in such applications as electrical insulation. As ever, there is no evidence that they are carcinogenic, other than the unfortunate specially bred rodents.

PCBs are closely associated with dioxins in the epidemiological demonology. All direct attempts to relate them to cancer have come to nought and serious studies give no support whatever to this idea. Here is an example

Study shows no PCB-cancer correlation

By Renate D. Kimbrough

Our study was the largest ever of workers occupationally exposed to PCBs. It includes all of the 7,075 men and women who worked for at least 90 days between 1946 and June 15, 1977, at the General Electric plants in Hudson Falls and Fort Edward.

There was no increase in deaths due to cancer or any other disease. The death rate due to all types of cancer was at or significantly below the expected level, based on national and regional averages.

Our study had an average follow-up time of 31 years; some employees were followed for as long as 50 years. If PCB exposure were to result in chronic health problems for these employees, I believe the problems would have been apparent during this long latency period. They were not.. ....

It is interesting that in the article from which the above is an extract, the author had to deal with an *ad hominem* attack of the usual ilk:

Finally, Mr. LeBrun refers to me as a "GE-paid" researcher. I do not work for GE and never have. I spent nearly 30 years in government service at the Centers for Disease Control, the Food and Drug Administration and the Environmental Protection Agency. Dr. Martha Doemland, who earned her doctorate at the State University at Buffalo and assisted with the study, also does not work for GE.

We work at the nonprofit Institute for Evaluating Health Risks, as the senior medial associate and an epidemiologist, respectively. The institute conducted the study at the request of and with funding from GE. It receives funding in approximately equal parts from government agencies and private-sector organizations.

I am paid a salary; my compensation is not dependent upon GE nor upon the results of any study I perform.

GE had no role of any kind in the conduct of the study, the evaluation of the data or the conclusions drawn. Our work was overseen by a panel of distinguished scientists from government and academia, none of whom are associated with GE or with our organization.

I believe the conclusions of our study are quite significant; they should allay fears that routine environmental exposure or even heavy occupational exposure to PCBs is associated with cancer or other serious illnesses.

Renate D. Kimbrough is a medical doctor associated with the Institute for Evaluating Health Risks.

The cancer scare would not hold water so the mongers came up with a new one – endocrine disruptors. Scientists at Tulane University in New Orleans reported in the June 1996 issue of *Science* that mixtures of some weakly estrogenic chemicals were up to 1,600 times more active than the compounds alone. These reports, coupled with research showing that exposure to various endocrine-disrupting pollutants was associated with reproductive problems in wildlife – including decreased penis sizes in alligators living in a contaminated Florida lake – galvanized scientific and public concern about environmental oestrogen.

Among others Stephen Scape, Professor of Toxicology at Texas A&M University commented:

> *Some scientists – including me – were skeptical. We pointed out that the human diet contains significant quantities of estrogenic chemicals--including phytoestrogens in fruits, vegetables and nuts, which have generally been associated with health benefits, including protection from some hormone-related cancers. Estrogenic hormones are used with great success by millions of postmenopausal women as hormone-replacement therapy, and the antiestrogenic compound tamoxifen is used as the first line of defense for the treatment of women with breast cancer. Moreover, birth-control pills and several other hormonally active drugs are used for treating prostate cancer and other diseases. The dietary intake of natural estrogenic compounds in various foods and estrogenic drugs used in pharmaceuticals far outweighs exposure to trace dietary levels of xenoestrogens.*

So, what happened about the Tulane study published in *Science* that so excited the media? Subsequent work in several other laboratories failed to produce any evidence of the effects the study had hypothesised. In the July 25, 1997, issue of *Science*, the Tulane scientists formally withdrew their original paper, acknowledging that they "have not been able to replicate our initial results."

And so it goes on. The evidence against PCBs and other so-called endocrine disruptors does not amount to a row of beans; yet legislation pours out, under the impetus of bodies such as the EPA. The cost of it all is millions of dollars that could have been applied to real health issues.

Chlorine

An article by four authors in the *JAMA* in 1996 tells it all:

Cholera Epidemic in U.S. Courtesy of EPA "Science"

In 1991, an epidemic of cholera started in Peru and spread to the rest of Latin America. This epidemic reached the U.S. in 1992 via an outbreak among 75 commercial airline passengers from Peru.

This epidemic is reported to have caused as many as 1 million cases of cholera and as many as 10,000 deaths.

Although the epidemic was reportedly started by a ship which dumped its bilge within reach of Peruvian waters, the epidemic's spread has been credited in part to the Peruvian government's decision to stop chlorinating drinking water supplies.

Why would the Peruvian government decide to forego such a basic public health measure as drinking water chlorination? (After all, chlorination has been used in the U.S. since 1908 and is generally considered as one of the greatest public health measures of all time!)

As first reported by the British journal Nature (November 28, 1991), the Peruvian government made the unfortunate, and ultimately fatal, mistake of ceasing chlorination based on EPA studies from the 1970s that associated drinking water chlorinated to 100 parts per billion with an increase in cancer risk for individuals on the order of 1 in 10,000.

It was not until 1992 that EPA's Science Advisory Board and EPA staff finally acknowledged that the link between chlorinated drinking water and cancer was not scientifically supportable.

Chlorination of water is perhaps the one intervention that has saved more human lives than any other, but this does not deter the scaremongers. In fact such epidemiological studies as have attempted to relate chlorine to cancer produce *relative risks* in the range 1.1 to 1.7, i.e. insignificant. Chlorine is essential to life, an essential component of blood plasma and digestive juices for example, yet Greenpeace brands it "Public enemy number one" and sent its supporters out with simple minded banners carrying such messages as "chlorine kills".

Pesticides

The environmental movement that started with Rachel Carson's influential book has been responsible for the deaths of millions of people, not only of malaria in Africa but of West Nile fever that started in New York before spreading to 49 states. Insects and rodents are the vectors for a wide range of diseases, many of them fatal, that afflict mankind. The environmentalists have carried on an unremitting battle against all pesticides. During the West Nile crisis in 1999, the New York Green Party said, "These diseases only kill the old and people whose health is already poor." What an unbelievably inhuman position to take! Yet it is a typical one. The ban on DDT, inspired by the EPA and forced upon the rest of the world, has killed millions of Africans, but they are only people. DDT is without doubt the iconic pesticide.

DDT

This insecticide was one of the greatest benign inventions in human history. The U.S. National Academy of Sciences once estimated that it had saved 500 million lives from malaria. It largely removed the threat of typhus.

Take Sri Lanka for example. In 1948 the annual malaria rate reached 2.8 million. By 1963, thanks to DDT, it had been reduced to just 17. By 1969 it was back to 2.5 million. What had happened in between? Well in 1962 Rachel Carson published *Silent Spring*, which triggered off a campaign that resulted in Sri Lanka banning DDT in 1964.

It would, of course, be foolish to rely on a single method of control, since the workings of evolution dictate that resistance will inevitably develop, but this one is cheap and highly effective, therefore ideal for poorer nations. The history of DDT and its eventual effective worldwide banning is an extraordinary one (see *Malaria and the DDT story*, Bibliography). It is naturally full of junk science and environmental extremism, a lack of any real scientific evidence, blackmail of poor countries by rich ones, a complete reversal of WHO policy as it was taken over by political correctness but, above all, an extraordinary disregard for human life.

And the rest

As you can see, this chapter is rapidly getting out of hand, and it has only touched the surface of an ocean of words and numbers on the purported beneficial or deleterious effects of the various substances. You could produce several weighty tomes on, for example, alcohol (which was given a whole chapter in *Sorry*); not all adverse as it "prevents" female heart disease among other things. The list of foods, drugs and chemicals claimed to be malign (or more rarely benign) is seemingly endless. Here is just a small selection of recent headlines:

Scientists say wood dust can cause cancer
Bread and crisps in cancer risk scare
Heart attack victims 'should drink tea'
'Cancer chemicals' in cod liver oil

Fears over tuna health risk to babies
Eggs may cut risk of breast cancer
Very low lead levels linked with IQ deficits
Premenopausal Fat Intake and Risk of Breast Cancer
Group links nail polish to birth defects
Pollution linked to birth defects
Wheat may prevent colon cancer
Why red wine is healthier
Cancer concern over vegetable nitrates
Beer Hops May Help Prevent Cancer
Chemicals linked to chronic fatigue
Deodorants linked to cancer

And so it goes on. Again, the above represents just as small fraction of the attribution of ills to various substances, and not a respectable relative risk among them, but there is one that dominates the world of epidemiology, politics and the media, the dreaded tobacco.

13. Tobacco Road

The road to hell is paved with good intentions
Proverb

It is rare for a single piece of scientific research to bring about profound change in human society. Albert Einstein was quite unique in that his first six papers all did just that in different ways. Others achieved great impact in human welfare, as our Time Chart shows. There was, however, one research result that heralded an unforeseeable upheaval in modern society. Though itself conducted with scientific rigour, it was indirectly to bring about the end of the scientific age, the birth of admonitory medicine, the creation of the Nanny State and the establishment of a risk-avoidance society wedded to the precautionary principle. In particular, it led to the creation of the new epidemiology.

The stories of tobacco and epidemiology in the second half of the 20th century are intertwined in a curious way. It often happens in human endeavours that the moment of triumph is also the moment at which decline begins. In science and engineering the moment of triumph occurred at the instant that a human foot first took a giant step onto the moon. Thereafter it was all downhill. There were, of course, further great technological advances to come, but the esprit that had made these activities the pinnacle of human achievement began to fade in the light of a new age of mysticism, while science and technology lost the status they enjoyed as the main engines for human development.

It was to be tobacco that provided the great breakthrough for statistical epidemiology but, like space exploration, it perhaps raised expectations and ambitions that could not be fulfilled. So the great white hope of medical science rapidly descended into quackery and deceit. Let us first examine the moment of triumph.

Austin Bradford Hill

After the Second World War one of the most urgent medical puzzles was the fact that lung cancer had increased by a factor of 15 in the last 25 years. One hypothesis at the time, a not very popular one, was that the causative factor was tobacco. It is difficult for anyone brought up in the era of political correctness to realise what a startling proposition this was. Tobacco was firmly embedded in social (and, indeed, sexual) behaviour. It had proved a remarkable reliever of stress during the war itself and cigarettes had been one of the essential supplies for the fighting men, as well as those enduring the bombardments at home. Younger people now seeing films of the period are startled by the ready acceptance of cigarettes as a normal part of life and social intercourse. The Medical Research Council called on Austin Bradford Hill to investigate a possible link.

Hill was son of the distinguished physiologist, Sir Leonard Erskine Hill. After leaving Chigwell Grammar School he entered the Royal Naval Air Service. It was while serving in Aegean that he developed pulmonary tuberculosis and was sent home. The illness dashed his hope of taking up a career in medicine, but he used his convalescence to take an external degree in economics from London University. After graduating he received a grant from the Medical Research Council to investigate the relatively high mortality rate of young adults in country districts. In 1933 he was appointed Reader in Epidemiology and Vital Statistics at the London School of Hygiene and Tropical Medicine, and Professor of Medical Statistics in 1945.

Hill's methods were simplistic. This is not meant to be a derogatory remark, as one of the ultimate failings of epidemiology was due to an increasing statistical sophistication (the dictionary definition of which is adulteration or falsification). He had developed the idea of the randomised clinical trial, which he had applied with great success to the evaluation of streptomycin as a treatment for tuberculosis in preference to the orthodox collapse treatment of the lung that he had been subjected to decades before. In particular, he was able to highlight not only the initial efficacy of the drug, but also the subsequent development of resistance to it. With the development of further drugs, deaths from tuberculosis declined, which only served to highlight the simultaneous rise in lung cancer as a cause of death.

Bradford Hill's colleagues in the investigation were Edward Kennaway of Bart's and Percy Stock, the Government's chief medical statistician. Later Dr Richard Doll was recruited to the project. Apart from Kennaway they were sceptical of any connection. In those days British hospitals were well run, rather than inefficiently administered as they are today. A key member of the team was the "Lady Almoner", who would nowadays be called a medical social worker. In the spring of 1948 twenty of them, in hospitals around London, were detailed to interview 649 lung cancer patients and 649 matched controls with other diseases. The results, when they were collected, appeared to show a dose-response relationship, but the team were advised by the director of the Medical Research Council, Sir Harold Himsworth, to delay publication until they had further confirmation. This has been interpreted as a political move, but the results were not all that convincing. It was only at a consumption of 50 cigarettes a day that there appeared to a significant effect (RR 2.45) so they went back to the drawing board. In the mean time, however, a similar study was published in the USA, so they immediately published their results in the BMJ in September 1950 "Smoking and Carcinoma of the Lungs: Preliminary Report".

They had attempted to make their field observations resemble an experiment by controlling for certain variables such as gender, age, and general physical health. The results were, in fact, not all that impressive and were controversial. R A Fisher, in particular, attacked them in print and in speeches, claiming that only true experimental designs are capable of establishing empirical causality. Fisher was concerned with the issue of association versus causation that clouds the interpretation of any observational study. In his infamous constitutional hypothesis, he suggested that the smoking and lung cancer association could be explained by the confounding effects of a genotype that predisposed both to smoking and lung cancer. Data on twins were used to substantiate his claims that smoking behaviour was influenced by genetics.

It is now taken as a truism that Fisher was entirely wrong. He was not. Even after the subsequent addition of substantial data that strongly confirmed the association, it is not proven that smoking causes lung cancer, any more than fertiliser causes tomatoes. In gauging Fisher's reaction, you have to take into account that he was by trade a geneticist, who was well aware of the influence of heredity on disease. He was particularly incensed by the hysterical public reaction to the claims and the incorporation of them into a then new trend in state propaganda and nagging. He was also an inveterate pipe smoker (as were most leading scientists) and a consultant to the tobacco industry, which laid him open to *ad hominem* attacks, and indeed created a precedent whereby anyone who questioned the ensuing orthodoxy was automatically suspected of being in pay of that villainous industry.

Hill's response to the criticisms was to come up with a new approach, the prospective rather than retrospective study. He established a number of criteria that would have to be met:

> 1. Strength (is the risk so large that we can easily rule out other factors?)
> 2. Consistency (have the results been replicated by different researchers and under different conditions?)
> 3. Specificity (is the exposure associated with a very specific disease as opposed to a wide range of diseases?)
> 4. Temporality (did the exposure precede the disease?)
> 5. Biological gradient (are increasing exposures associated with increasing risks of disease?)
> 6. Plausibility (is there a credible scientific mechanism that can explain the association?)
> 7. Coherence (is the association consistent with the natural history of the disease?)
> 8. Experimental evidence (does a physical intervention show results consistent with the association?)
> 9. Analogy (is there a similar result that we can draw a relationship to?)

These are of course, fairly robust criteria and if epidemiologists had stuck to them there would be no call for the book you are reading now, but, as we have seen, they did not.

The question remains as to whether they establish causality. Let us return to an imaginary experiment that has already been adumbrated. Say you tried to grow tomatoes on poor soil and failed to get any fruit at all. You then experiment with different doses of potassium rich fertiliser. What you find is that tomatoes appear and the number and size increase with the dose. Have you proved that fertiliser causes tomatoes?

In this example we know that the answer is no, because we understand the mechanism by which tomatoes grow from seeds. What if you omit the planting of the tomato seeds? In a case such as cancer we do not know the mechanism. Substances such as tobacco might merely act as the fertiliser. The cause, if there is indeed one at all, is still unknown. We might surmise all different sorts of causes. It could be, for example, evolution. A gene's survival might well be promoted if the older bearers of it are killed off at the stage when they become a burden to the tribe. Since old women are more useful than old men, because of their child rearing skills, it might well promote survival if they stayed around a bit longer, which they do indeed.

The names of the great double acts resonate down the halls of history – Burke and Hare, Laurel and Hardy, Kruschev and Bulganin. To them must be added the illustrious progenitors of the new epidemiology, Hill and Doll. Doll was the junior member of the team and, like his leader, was originally dubious about an association between tobacco and lung cancer. Hill's great innovation was to base his prospective study on a cohort of 60,000 medical practitioners, 40,000 of whom responded to his initial letter in the *British Medical Journal*.

Over a period of 11 years, Doll and Hill found 7 lung cancer deaths per hundred thousand men per year among non-smokers, but 166 per year among heavy smokers. This is 24 times as many! For heart attacks the corresponding figures were 599 for heavy smokers and 422 for non-smokers. While these figures do not look nearly as dramatic, the effect on heart disease is perhaps more important. Apparently there were 166 - 7 = 159 excess deaths per hundred thousand per year from lung cancer and 599 - 422 = 177 excess deaths per hundred thousand per year from heart attacks that might be ascribed to smoking.

But look at the figures from another angle. What Doll and Hill reported was that annually 99,993 nonsmokers out of every 100,000 people escape death from lung cancer as opposed to 99,834 smokers per 100,000 who are so lucky (subtracting seven nonsmoker deaths and 166 smoker deaths from 100,000 respectively). When we divide the smaller number by the larger number, we get a smoking vs. nonsmoking "survival factor" of approximately 0.998. This, remember, is on an annual basis and over a lifetime it would be more like 0.92.

"What this means is that, while a person who smokes may indeed incur a 24 times greater risk of dying from lung cancer than a person who doesn't smoke, the smoker also has 99.8 percent of the nonsmoker's chance of *not* dying from lung cancer. But only the "24 times as likely" risk was considered by the surgeon general. Why?" These are the questions raised by Don Oakley in his book *Slow Burn*.

In these days of perpetual hype, it is difficult to find words to convey the effects of the establishment of the link between cigarette smoking and lung cancer. It is no exaggeration to say that it changed the world, and not necessarily for the better. The fact that something that was securely established as a factor in the majority of adult lifestyles could apparently cause a fatal disease was new and startling. What was not so obvious was the uniqueness of this particular result. Never again was such a large effect to be identified. Some of the results of the study can be enumerated.

1. A growing number of researchers would come to pin their hopes of fame on finding a similar nugget. It was the beginning of a massive expansion in universities and everyone was looking for their research niche. The desperation of many of them would prove to change the face of the new science of epidemiology. There would a flood of bad science and even fraud (much of it probably undetected).

2. It gave politicians and bureaucrats the first real excuse they had for intervening in the everyday habits of ordinary people since the Gin Act of 1751. It provided the foundation of the Nanny State. Institutional nagging backed up by draconian taxation would eventually become the order of the day. A whole new shaft of excuses for burdensome tax increases was opened up.

3. If one lifestyle factor caused disease, why should not others? A question that was to provide the rationale for the social medicine movement and change forever the way that medicine was practised.

4. Although Political Correctness was still in the future, tobacco would be a keystone in its construction. Tobacco would become its most evil icon. The suppression of tobacco would be the measure of its power. By the end of the century, which was then only half way through, more than 70,000 papers would be published, most of them rubbish, on the evils of tobacco, and the few brave or misguided souls who persisted in its use would become social pariahs.

5. American lawyers, who already had that great nation enslaved for their own benefit, would begin to conceive of billions of dollars of potential income through the corrupt and incompetent legal system of that benighted country. The rest of the world would slavishly follow.

6. The tobacco companies, who were used to luxuriating in a vast and guaranteed income, would be forced onto the defensive and would be reduced to despicable ploys to preserve their interests.

7. It gradually became an established principle that it was the duty of everyone, individuals and state, to preserve life as long as possible. Regardless of whether it ended in neglect, incontinence and dementia, what mattered was the quantity of life, not the quality. It was a dramatic re-establishment of the Puritan ethic, but with saving the body replacing saving the soul.

8. Cancer epidemiology would take on aspects of a religion, even down to the classic schism, with dietists and environmentalists hurling shrill insults at each other across the barrier.
9. The first modern groups of SIFs would be formed, (earlier SIF groups include Anti-Vivisectionists, the Soil Association, Vegetarian Society, Eugenics League etc.) which would lead to a spread of this type of behaviour.
10. The vital independence of science would be lost and a complex trail of events would be set off that would end in dire consequences, such as millions of people dying of malaria.

It is clear that Hill, ironically like his erstwhile opponent Fisher, came to realise that he had created a monster. Towards the end of his life he began to complain about the proliferation of poorly regulated studies. Little did he know that this was only a small beginning, and that the conservative principles that he had laid down would simply be abandoned by his inheritors, even his own protégé.

There was blood in the water and the sharks were circling, not only the notorious American personal injury lawyers, who were always on the look out for a nice little earner, but all the hangers on, such as those who hankered after expert witness fees or those who wanted a few publications to their name and some media coverage to keep the university public relations department happy.

Fast Forward

It would be excessive to try to summarise the 70,000 plus papers on the evils of tobacco. It would turn this book into a single-issue compendium. Rather than wade through even a small selection of them, it is more illustrative to move forward half a century too see how the climate had changed. So let us look at just one recent example from 2003:

Association of Pediatric Dental Caries With Passive Smoking

C. Andrew Aligne, MD, MPH; Mark E. Moss, DDS, PhD; Peggy Auinger, MS; Michael Weitzman, MD ; *JAMA.* 2003;289:1258-1264.

Here are the results of the "research":

> *Twenty-five percent of the children had at least 1 unfilled decayed tooth surface and 33% had at least 1 filled surface. Fifty-three percent had cotinine levels consistent with passive smoking. Elevated cotinine level was significantly associated with both decayed (odds ratio [OR], 2.1; 95% confidence interval [CI], 1.5-2.9) and filled (OR, 1.4; 95% CI, 1.1-1.8) tooth surfaces in deciduous but not in permanent teeth. This relationship persisted after adjusting for age, sex, race, family income, geographic region, frequency of dental visits, and blood lead level. For dental caries in deciduous teeth, the adjusted OR was 1.8 (95% CI, 1.2-2.7) for the risk of decayed surfaces and 1.4 (95% CI, 1.1-2.0) for filled surfaces. We*

estimated the population attributable risk from passive smoking to be 27% for decayed and 14% for filled tooth surfaces.

And here are some of the headlines it generated:

Cavities tied to passive smoking in study
Passive smoke tied to dental woes in kids
Cavities in kids linked to second-hand smoke
Smoke harms kids' teeth
Smokes rot kids' teeth, says study
Study: Second-hand cigarette smoke causes cavities in children

By this stage the reader should readily appreciate that the story has more holes than the teeth. If not, they might wish to consider that:

1. The *significance* and *relative risks* are at levels not normally accepted in real science.
2. Dental caries and smoking are both strongly associated with poverty and poor education.
3. **Cotinine** *is produced by the metabolisation of* **nicotine**. *Here is what* Sorry, wrong number! *had to say about nicotine:*
   > *By the way, talking of nasty substances, nicotine is found in many common vegetables (potatoes, tomatoes, aubergines etc.) as well as tea. It is estimated (Med Sci Res. 1993, 21, 571-572) that eating a normal portion of potatoes equals three-and-a-half hours in a smoky room.*
4. What possible mechanism could cause the order of one part per billion of any substance in the blood to bore holes in the teeth?
5. Correlation is not causation.
6. Propaganda is propaganda is propaganda.

But the really startling aspect of this publication is revealed when you look into the connections of the authors. They actually comprise a firm that is organized to exploit the officially sponsored extortion from the tobacco industry. Dr Andrew Aligne collects the money from a "non-profit" organisation called Pediathink. Its web site blurb includes the statement that "Americans' confidence in nonprofits has dropped precipitously, leading to the lowest level of charitable giving ever recorded, according to a 2002 Epsilon survey. In order to regain the public's trust, nonprofits must focus not just on improving organizational efficiency, but also on making sure that programs are having a real impact." He is also a member of the International Tobacco Control Directory. Among his unfounded claims are:

> *The loss of life from tobacco-related, pediatric illnesses accounts for $4.6 billion per year for direct medical expenditures, resulting from more than 5.4 million excess cases of disease.*

Sudden infant death syndrome (SIDS) results in more than 5500 deaths per year in the US. Exposure to tobacco smoke accounts for almost 2000 cases of SIDS each year, with a loss of life cost of $2.7 billion.

The most common bacterial infection, acute otitis media, is the most frequently diagnosed ailment in children. There are 3.4 million cases of acute otitis media attributable to involuntary smoking, at a cost of $150 million annually.

Asthma leads to 13 million contacts with physicians, 200,000 hospitalizations, and more than 100 deaths among children annually. The estimated costs attributable to ETS are $180 million for direct medical expenditures and $19 million for loss of life.

Dr Moss and his assistant, Peggy Auinger, are the "researchers". Michael Weitzman is a prolific publisher of papers on child health, a member of the Tobacco Consortium. He served as an expert witness for the US Department of Justice in a trial against the tobacco industry and took a major role in informing EPA policy by assembling what is "known" about the effects of environmental toxins on children.

That, of course, was just passive smoking. With active smoking no association, however bizarre, is excluded. From the *Independent*:

Smoking 'can make babies badly behaved'

By Steve Connor, Science Editor

02 April 2003

Pregnant women who smoke heavily risk having children who are badly behaved, a study into the effects of tobacco on the development of babies suggests.

The research found that children of mothers who smoked more than 20 cigarettes a day throughout their pregnancies were more likely to be disruptive and antisocial at primary school age.

Professor Terrie Moffitt of the Institute of Psychiatry, King's College London, said the findings could only be explained by smoking rather than other known risk factors for antisocial behaviour such as poverty, social class and low birth rate.

One theory was that there was something in cigarette smoke – perhaps nicotine – that affected the developmental genes involved in the growth or maturity of the foetal brain, she said.

The research, which has not yet been published in a peer-reviewed scientific journal, involved studying the school reports of more than 1,116 sets of identical and non-identical twins as well as interviews with their mothers.

Although smoking during pregnancy is known to be bad for the health of the foetus, this is the first study to suggest it might also cause behavioural problems.

There is no doubt that both Fisher and Bradford Hill, though implacable opponents, would have been horrified, not only by the standards of statistical practice involved in such publications, but also by the financial web woven around them. Of course, such behaviour would have been less opprobrious if their side had not been the first to fling out *ad hominem* accusations of pecuniary interest or if they had actually practised good science. How could it all have come about? To see why, we have to go back a decade in time.

Flash Back

In fact, it all started even further back in 1971, when Nixon declared war on cancer. Nixon had a bad press. OK, he was a crook, but then he was a politician. Compared with the Kennedys he was a knight in shining armour. His greatest problems were that he had to deal with a hostile Congress and antagonistic media.

One of the truly big lies of epidemiology is that 90% of cancers are environmental in origin. That extreme claim was attributed to John Bailar III, but similar ones with various percentages have been around for decades. There is no evidence to substantiate any of them, but it was such thinking that led to the creation of the Environmental Protection Agency. Foundation of the EPA was one of the things Nixon wished to be remembered for. It was founded on a lie and so it had to be sustained by that lie, which leads us to:

The greatest scientific fraud ever

In 1988 the EPA had begun to formulate legislation banning smoking in public places. This was being done out of pure politically correct zeal, but the realisation dawned that some "scientific evidence" was going to be needed to justify it. The organisation therefore began to produce the evidence of a link between passive smoking and lung cancer, in what they called a *metastudy* (as observed in Chapter 7, grouping together a number of disparate findings to produce one result, i.e. forging a strong chain out of a number of weak links). Unfortunately, this did not work, as the required association was not at all evident. They then omitted a major contribution that had produced a negative result; still no joy. Getting desperate, they then took the outrageous decision to change the standards of significance by abandoning the already dubious epidemiological standard of $P<0.05$ in favour of an unheard of $P<0.1$, i.e. a one in ten chance of the result being a pure statistical accident. The truly amazing thing is that, even after all these shenanigans, they only managed to produce a *relative risk* of a pathetic 1.19, but they published it anyway in 1992.

Fast forward again

So what was the result of the launch of the greatest ever scientific fraud upon the world? Though it was exposed over and over again in articles and books, the establishment simply ignored the criticism and it became official doctrine that passive smoking caused a 20% increase in lung cancer risk.

Cancer will kill 5 million British smokers yelled the headline in *The Times*, June 25th, 2001. The number comes from one Sir Richard Peto (a name, as we shall see, to conjure with). It only applies, of course, unless ministers intensify efforts to help people to quit. Having taken on board all the fiddles that were invented by CDC in America, Britain's big numbers man adds on a bit then extrapolates over 50 years to get a really impressive total.

Never coy about scientific and statistical niceties, he goes on "There are about ten million smokers in Britain and about five million will be killed by tobacco if they do not stop." This set a new record for anti-tobacco claims, raising the claimed hit rate to a startling 50%.

Fellow SIF, Professor Gordon McVie, added his piece for the rest of the world, where tobacco is going to kill one billion people "...the challenge for the developing world is to make sure it does not make the same mistakes that we have, by becoming ensnared in a cancer-causing life-style of fags, booze and junk food." Presumably it is all right to carry on taking the junk science.

The big push came when eighteen presidents of medical institutions wrote to *The Times* on November 25th 2003 demanding a ban on smoking in public places.

> Sir, We believe that the time has come for legislation to make public places smoke-free. Passive smoking causes an estimated 1,000 deaths in adults each year and causes asthma, lung infections and middle ear disease in children.....

It is a remarkable testament to the power of political correctness that the entire medical establishment should unite to repeat an outrageous lie. The claims about the body count from passive smoking derive originally from that so-called meta-study conducted by the US EPA in 1992, but there were many others "linking" passive smoking to all the ills of mankind. As we have seen, there are at least five cold-blooded statistical frauds in the EPA study. If you strip them out, it clearly shows that environmental tobacco smoke is harmless (as did a more recent, properly conducted, but much vilified, study).

As we know, this is not a unique example of the way the medical establishment has parted company with real science (other prominent examples are salt and cholesterol) but it is their most egregious attempt to substitute coercion for liberty. They obviously envied the strides made by PC authoritarians in such places as California, New York and Ireland.

It is well known, but not allowed to be repeated publicly, that tobacco, like alcohol, is a great reliever of stress. It is also often stated that more than half of visits to GPs relate to stress-induced disease. People who resume smoking frequently do so in response to stress; and a controlled, bureaucratised society is a particularly stressful one in which to live. Tobacco is also a great aid to cerebration and most of the notable scientists in pre-PC days were inveterate pipe smokers; their achievements speak for themselves.

In November 2003, scientists at the University of Houston were vilified for announcing that nicotine repairs damaged brain function. Karim Alkadhi, associate professor of pharmacology, and his team of researchers at the UH College of Pharmacy established that nicotine has a beneficial effect and, in many cases, even repairs memory impairment caused by stress on the brain. Such rash attempts at putting science above political correctness are, however, comparatively rare and there is almost no known disease that has not been attributed by some epidemiologist to tobacco.

As this book was ready to go to press in April 2004, the crescendo of propaganda by the worldwide anti-smoking zealots had reached a climax. They had grown increasingly shameless in their abuse of science and the statistical method. The *RR* was 1.15 for the claim that partners of smokers die earlier, and this was achieved by ignoring the glaring confounding factors that cigarette smoking is correlated with low social status and is a well-known response to stress. The only remarkable thing about this correlation is that it is so low. **Passive smoking blamed for deaths** cried the BBC. **Partners of smokers die younger** yelled *The Times,* with a sub-heading that claimed a cut of 15% in life expectancy (i.e. about eleven years). **Passive smoking dangers revealed** screams the AOL news page. This one came with the imprimatur of the Harvard School of Public Health, the home of junk statistics.

The other story, released at the same time and even more bizarre, came from the Dark State of Insanity. The University of California told us that people who live with smokers heal more slowly from cuts and bruises, no numbers given. **How smokers harm healing** trumpeted *The Telegraph*. **Half an hour in a smoky pub could trigger heart attack** yelled *The Independent*, quoting a particularly vacuous piece of propaganda from the CDC.

As if it were all an unorchestrated series of events, we had the statement from Deborah Arnott of ASH: **The case for a new law to end smoking in the workplace and in enclosed public places is now overwhelming.** Having conquered the lunatic fringe (California, New York and Ireland) they were set on world domination.
It was, however, the linking of tobacco with the most feared of human catastrophes, cancer, that was to have the profound effect on society that would change it forever in so many ways, as we have observed above; so let us see how cancer was approached.

14. Cancer!

Orthodox medicine has not found an answer to your complaint. However, luckily for you, I happen to be a quack.
Richter cartoon caption

The linking of tobacco with lung cancer was a two-pronged affair. It not only cast tobacco in the role of the ultimate demon, it also highlighted cancer as the route to fame and fortune for the growing ranks of the new scientists. Millions of rats and mice would be sacrificed on the altar of the new epidemiology, having absurd quantities and concentrations painted onto them or fed into them. Questionnaires and surveys would proliferate beyond the bounds of reason. No stone (or substance) would be left unturned in the frantic search for the new tobacco and the glittering prizes. For cancer was, rightly, dreaded by the populace. A third of us are going to contract it and a quarter of us die from it. It is fearful thing, and fear is there to be exploited by the ruthless. Let us have a look at some of the things blamed for cancer.

The complete list of things that give you cancer (according to epidemiologists)

Abortion, acetaldehyde, acrylamide, acrylonitril, agent orange, alar, alcohol, air pollution, aldrin, alfatoxin, arsenic, arsine, asbestos, asphalt fumes, atrazine, AZT, baby food, benzene, benzidine, benzopyrene, beryllium, beta-carotene, betel nuts, birth control pills, bottled water, bracken, bread, breasts, calcium channel blockers, cadmium, captan, carbon black, carbon tetrachloride, careers for women, casual sex, car fumes, celery, charred foods, chewing gum, Chinese food, Chinese herbal supplements, chloramphenicol, chlordane, chlorinated camphene, chlorinated water, chlorodiphenyl, chloroform, cholesterol, low cholesterol, chromium, coal tar, coffee, coke ovens, crackers, creosote, cyclamates, dairy products, deodorants, depleted uranium, depression, dichloryacetylene, DDT, dieldrin, diesel exhaust, diet soda, dimethyl sulphate, dinitrotoluenene, dioxin, dioxane, epichlorhydrin, ethyl acrilate, ethylene, ethilene dibromide, ethnic beliefs, ethylene dichloride, Ex-Lax, fat, fluoridation, flying, formaldehyde, free radicals, fruit, gasoline, genes, gingerbread, global warming, gluteraldehyde, granite, grilled meat, Gulf war, hair dyes, hamburgers, heliobacter pylori, hepatitis B virus, hexachlorbutadiene, hexachlorethane, high bone mass, HPMA, HRT, hydrazine, hydrogen peroxide, incense, infertility, jewellery, Kepone, kissing, lack of exercise, laxatives, lead, left handedness, Lindane, Listerine, low fibre diet, magnetic fields, malonaldehyde, mammograms, manganese, marijuana, methyl bromide, methylene chloride, menopause, microwave ovens, milk hormones, mixed spices, mobile phones, MTBE, nickel, night lighting, night shifts, nitrates, not breast feeding, not having a twin, nuclear power plants, Nutrasweet, obesity, oestrogen, olestra, olive oil, orange juice, oxygenated gasoline, oyster sauce, ozone, ozone depletion, passive smoking, PCBs, peanuts, pesticides, pet birds, plastic IV bags, polio vaccine, potato crisps (chips), power lines, proteins, Prozac, PVC, radio masts, radon, railway sleepers, red meat, Roundup, saccharin, salt, selenium, semiconductor plants, shellfish, sick buildings, soy sauce, stress, strontium, styrene, sulphuric acid, sun beds, sunlight, sunscreen, talc, tetrachloroethylene, testosterone, tight bras, toast, toasters, tobacco, tooth fillings, toothpaste (with fluoride or bleach), trichloroethylene, under-arm shaving, unvented stoves, uranium, vegetables, vinyl bromide, vinyl chloride, vinyl fluoride, vinyl toys, vitamins, vitreous fibres, wallpaper, weedkiller (2-4 D), welding fumes, well water, weight gain, wood dust, work, x-rays.

Actually, to be honest, the list is not quite complete, as some substances with very long names and numbers have been omitted, but you get the general idea.

Another effect of the linkage was the beatification of Richard Doll. Hill's once humble research assistant was elected FRCP in 1957 and FRS in 1966. He was knighted in 1971 and made a Companion of Honour in 1996. He received the United Nations Award for cancer research in 1962, the BMA's Gold medal in 1983, the Royal Society Royal Medal in 1986 and the Gold Medal of the European Society of Cardiology in 2000. He received honorary degrees from thirteen universities. The most significant action by Doll, however, was his treatment of the criteria laid down by his mentor, Hill, mentioned in the last chapter. Once free of Hill's restraining influence, he simply kicked over the traces and ignored them. He thus became one of the prime movers in the foundation of the new epidemiology, which all came to a head in 1981 with the publication of the little red book.

The causes of cancer

This was the title of the book written by Richard Doll and Richard Peto and published by Oxford Medical Publications. It is an overtly impressive production, crammed with tables, diagrams and no fewer than five appendices. Irritatingly small print and an opaque literary style made for hard reading, but its impact was enormous and it spawned whole new industries of dietetics and bureaucratic nannying. It reigned supreme and unchallenged for a couple of decades, until James Le Fanu published his monumental *Rise and fall of modern medicine* in 1999, but by then the cancer industry was so well established that it was able simply to ignore this upstart who sought to restore science to medicine. A core theme of *The causes of cancer* is comparisons between a population in Connecticut and other parts of the world. Here is the Le Fanu take on it:

> *The Causes of Cancer may look impressive, but appearances can be deceptive. The intellectual rigour required by Sir Richard Doll's mentor, Sir Austin Bradford Hill, for assessing the coherence of any hypothesised relationship between an environmental factor and disease – such as food and cancer – is conspicuous only by its absence. Thus the distinguishing feature between the Western diet, as eaten in Connecticut, and that of other countries, such as India, is the relatively high consumption of meat and dairy products. Hence cancers common in the West, such as those of the breast, colon and pancreas, are attributed to a 'high-fat' diet. True or false? The Mormons and Seventh-Day Adventists are identical in virtually every way: they lead sober lives, don't smoke or drink and go to church on Sundays. The only difference is that the Mormons eat meat and the Seventh-Day Adventists on the whole are vegetarians. If the 'high-fat' diet explanation for cancer was valid, then the meat-eating Mormons must by definition have a higher incidence of these cancers than the Seventh-Day Adventists. But they do not. Such an important observation in the context of a report in which diet is strongly incriminated in cancer requires serious consideration. There is none.*

Even more importantly Le Fanu homes in on a vital and quite astonishing statement almost buried at the end of the second chapter on **Evidence for the avoidability of cancer**:

> Turning finally to the role of age itself, it is sometimes suggested that because cancer is ten or a hundred times more likely to occur in the old rather than the young then ageing per se might be thought of as an important determinant of cancer. We rather doubt whether this viewpoint is a scientifically fruitful one, and in any case we are concerned in this report with avoidable causes of cancer, among which we can hardly count old age.

This obscure paragraph is so loaded with meaning that it merits a few direct comments:

1. Ten or a hundred is a gross underestimate, the ratio is more like a thousand to one.

2. As Le Fanu observes " On the contrary it is scientifically very fruitful, for recognising the primacy of ageing as a powerful determinant of cancer is essential if one is not to fall into the trap of generating false notions about what else might be the cause."

3. This is an example of the logical fallacy known as *Begging the question*, in which the truth of the conclusion is assumed by the premises. The whole book is concerned with trying to establish that some cancers are avoidable, yet the idea that they are avoidable is used as a justification for ignoring, at the outset, the overriding dominant factor.

4. When one factor is so dominant, any errors associated with estimating its contribution will outweigh the whole contribution of the other factors.

5. The concept of avoidability is loaded with assumptions that might or might not be correct. For example, that cancer must have an identifiable cause. An atom of radium is known to be unstable, with a half-life of 1620 years, but no one can predict precisely when it will suddenly produce its quantum of gamma radiation and emanation of radon. DNA lesions are known to occur in human cells at an astonishing rate and there must be a highly effective repair mechanism. It is a possibility that such a mechanism would decline in efficacy with age. As we observed in chapter 6, man is a tool-maker and has a propensity always to look for a purpose or a cause, when there might well be none.

Here is just one of the many tables, taken from the first appendix of this book, which purports to explain the process by which the age factor is eliminated.

TABLE A2.—Example: *Calculation of age-standardized lung[a] cancer death certification rates among males in 1977*

Age range No.	Age range Years	No. of 1977 male deaths certified as being due to lung[a] cancer at indicated ages[b]	Estimated[c] male population in indicated age range in mid-1977 (thousands)	Annual age-specific male lung[a] cancer death certification rates/1000	Weight (based on U.S. 1970 census; see table A1)	Product: age-specific rate × weight	Annual age-standardized death certification rate/1000
1	0–4	2	8,090	0.0002	84416	21	—
2	5–9	5	9,051	0.0006	98204	54	—
3	10–14	2	9,922	0.0002	102304	21	—
4	15–19	10	10,896	0.0009	93845	86	—
5	20–24	24	10,404	0.0023	80561	186	—
6	25–29	55	9,378	0.0059	66320	389	—
7	30–34	147	8,016	0.0183	56249	1032	—
8	35–39	423	6,397	0.0661	54656	3614	—
9	40–44	1,119	5,740	0.1949	58958	11494	—
10	45–49	2,921	5,879	0.4969	59622	29623	—
11	50–54	5,780	5,863	0.9858	54643	53869	—
12	55–59	8,607	5,425	1.5865	49077	77863	—
13	60–64	11,495	4,500	2.5544	42403	108316	—
14	65–69	12,987	3,704	3.5062	34406	120635	—
15	70–74	11,479	2,592	4.4286	26789	118638	—
16	75–79	7,972	1,648	4.8374	18871	91286	—
17	80–84	4,241	1,018	4.1660	11241	46830	—
18	≥85	2,038	674	3.0237	7435	22481	—
1–13	0–64	30,590	99,561	—	901258	286568	0.31796[d]
14–18	>65	38,717	9,636	—	98742	399871	4.0497[d]
1–18	All ages	69,307[f]	109,197[e]	—	1000000	686439	0.6864[d]

If you have looked through this table you might wonder what is going on. Welcome to the club! Having coped in the past with subjects such as special relativity, quantum mechanics or extremal statistics, I thought I could wrestle with most mathematical problems, but after a couple of dozen readings I still do not understand this. Why should rates based on 1977 figures be weighted according to a 1970 census, and by some derivation not defined? The averages are already weighted by the estimates of population and if those estimates are awry the errors are transmitted through the calculation, weighted or not. Talking of errors, even within the favoured under 65 group, a 5% error in calculating the 60-64 figure would virtually wipe out the entire contribution of the under forties. Even after all the weighting it would only take a 1% error to wipe out the under thirties. These are not large variations in such populations and could arrive through such factors as difficulties of diagnosis and masking by other diseases.

Furthermore, if such evidence were offered by an undergraduate in engineering or physical science, it would be thrown back with a request for an explanation as to why data to a precision down to single figures are multiplied by weightings precise to six significant figures and for justification for presenting the final averages to a precision of five figures. That would be pretty good going even for a high precision instrumentation system, but for statistics on human populations? Unwarranted precision is one of the hallmarks of misleading or misguided science. In such an application two figures of precision would normally be regarded as pushing your luck.

So, what did all this manipulation achieve? We can calculate an ordinary unweighted raw average from columns 3 and 4 and then see how much all these calculations have changed it.

It all seems rather a lot of effort to make an adjustment to the figures of between 0.8 and 8 per cent. Since the book is rather dismissive of the significance of deaths in the older group, the relevant change is **three percent**. Most people working in applied statistics would regard this as rather a sterile exercise producing an insignificant change. This is because they are not epidemiologists and therefore do not understand. For, as these authors state,

> These propositions are generally accepted by all competent epidemiologists (though not by all propagandists), and we would like to see it equally widely accepted that it is also dangerous to make inferences from trends in overall standardised cancer rates if these trends are due chiefly to trends among older people and are not also evident upon the examination of standardized rates among people under 65.

Interesting vocabulary for a scientific treatise, dividing the world of science into competent epidemiologists and propagandists! You might think it is a prime example of the proud man's contumely. More humble scientists, such as Albert Einstein, did not treat the rest of the world with contempt; they tried to explain.

In fact, you might well come to the conclusion that the whole thing is a classic example of *misdirection*, the conjuror's patter that distracts from the sleight of hand that he is practising.

The rest of the book is of the same calibre. By such devices as employing the *concentration fallacy* and ignoring the first *principle of toxicology*, all sorts of chemicals, foodstuffs, environmental factors and jobs are in the frame. The book did more than any other to enshrine the procedures of the new epidemiology, and its successors would go on to such achievements as calculating with great precision the cancer risks of eating celery or the cancer preventive properties of tomatoes. In other chapters of this book just a tiny fraction of these effusions have been mentioned.

Again, this chapter could easily become encyclopaedic, but rather repetitive. One insignificant statistical result is very like any other; so let us instead have a look at what happened when epidemiologists were really let loose on the world.

15. Holocaust

No flocks that range the valley free
To slaughter I condemn
Taught by the power that pities me,
I learn to pity them.
Goldsmith – The Hermit

Onset

Monday February 19th 2001 was a day much as any other for veterinary surgeon Craig Kirby, as he began a routine inspection of the pigs at an abattoir in Little Warley near Brentwood in Essex. Because of the wholesale closure of local facilities, due to the over-zealous application of European Union hygiene rules by British civil servants, by this time animals were travelling cruelly long distances to be killed. This in itself was an inhumane outrage, but it was to pale into insignificance with the nastiness yet to come. These pigs, which had come from Buckinghamshire and the Isle of Wight, had been showing signs of lethargy, so the vet was particularly careful in his examination, during which he noticed blisters.

The last epidemic of foot and mouth (FMD) had taken place in 1967, before he was born, but he identified the symptoms and immediately called the ministry (MAFF).
The Ministry for Agriculture Fisheries and Food had achieved a certain notoriety long before these events. They had exhibited a mixture of incompetence, arrogance and complacency that seemed to typify all that was worst in the Great British Bureaucrat. They had veered wildly from suppressing evidence of real dangers to implementing senseless bans on such things as Roseclear and beef-on-the-bone. Two years before this particular crisis, I wrote in *Sorry, wrong number!* that they had been out of control for years. Not only was the mind-set of this organisation a recipe for disaster, its veterinary service had been savaged during the public expenditure cuts of the Thatcher Government and the number of vets was half what it had been.

34 years previously the outbreak of the disease had been confined to a small area in Cheshire and Shropshire, but now, thanks to the overweening bureaucracy and interventionist governments in London and Brussels, animals were being wretchedly transported hither and thither all over the country. By the Friday an outbreak had occurred at the run-down farm of two brothers in Northumberland.

The state of their husbandry earned them nomination by MAFF as the scapegoats for the whole disaster, though no evidence was adduced until much later. It is almost certain that the disease had been around for some time in sheep, which reveal few and relatively mild symptoms. Before the crisis was a week old, outbreaks were being investigated in Gloucestershire, Northern Ireland, Scotland, Devon and Wiltshire. By the end of the month I had posted on **Number Watch**, under the heading **mad, mad, mad!** my **Number of the Month** which was the number of animals slaughtered, 15,000. Little did we know that this was to become a drop in the ocean.

The state of the art

It would be salutary at this stage to examine the state of knowledge of the disease and its treatment, as it existed at the commencement of the outbreak. The world's leading laboratory in this field was the US Institute of Animal Health on Plumb Island, New York. Among its staff was one who was recognised as the leading authority, Professor Fred Brown, an Englishman and formerly the head of Britain's centre of expertise, the Pirbright Institute. In Europe the acknowledged expert was a Dutch vet, Dr Simon Barteling, who had been responsible for handling over 20 outbreaks of the disease in different parts of the world. Both these experts had worked with the most modern vaccines and had expressed their conviction that vaccination provided the key to rapid control of the disease without the need to resort to mass slaughter. Indeed, when an outbreak occurred in Albania and Macedonia in 1996, the EU, fearing a spread across its own borders, had quickly set up a vaccination programme. The outbreak was totally suppressed within a few weeks. Thus, it was not just theoretical knowledge, but practical experience with convincing results, that pointed to vaccination as being the only reasonable and effective way to tackle the disease: but the British establishment had its mind set on slaughter.

The growing crisis

As February gave way to March, the number of separate outbreaks had reached 32. Two days later, with articles in the press stating that it was unlikely to reach the proportions of the 1960s epidemic, it had got to 52, in areas as far apart as Cumbria, Dumfries, Lancashire, Herefordshire and the Isle of Wight. Four days on it was 81 and after one more day it was up to 96. MAFF's chief vet, Jim Scudamore, at this stage expressed confidence that "the number of outbreaks would begin to fall by the weekend". The killing fields were now operating in earnest and the number animals already or about to be slaughtered had reached 90,000.

By now Government orders had closed down the countryside, with all footpaths and bridleways blocked off throughout the nation. Not only farming, but entire rural industries, which had all suffered from Government policies ranging from indifference to downright hostility, were threatened with imminent bankruptcy. By March 11th the Minister responsible, Nick Brown, was "absolutely certain that the disease was under control – we are going to eliminate it." The number of outbreaks had now reached 161. Vast funeral pyres sent the last hopes of the farming industry reeking up to heaven. Carcasses waiting to be burnt lay bloated and putrid in the fields. Shreds of half burnt skin and flesh were wafted across the fields and into people's gardens.

In an even more bizarre move, MAFF decided that carcases would have to be taken to a rendering plant in Widnes, Lancashire. Infected animals were carted hundreds of miles through disease-free territory. The Prime Minister was in a dilemma. He had decided to cut and run for an election a year early, no doubt being aware that the economic boom would be unsustainable beyond the autumn. He had chosen May 3rd, a date that was looking more and more unlikely as the disaster progressed. By March 16th, with cases now at 240, MAFF really began to panic. They announced a policy of "contiguous cull" which meant that all animals within three kilometre zones around known cases would be slaughtered. 18th March, 303 cases, 20th March 343 cases, 21st March 411 cases. The opposition spokesman, Tim Yeo, accused the government of incompetence in not speeding up the slaughter, while Ben Gill, NFU President, pleaded with the Prime Minister for more efficient extermination.

Enter the epidemiologist (with his computer)

Professor Roy Anderson had suddenly turned up at in 1999 at Imperial College, having resigned a chair at Oxford in somewhat shady circumstances. The details do not concern us here, but suffice it to say that a meeting of 26 professors and readers in the Department of Zoology had met and passed a motion of no confidence in him. It was said that his autocratic style had made conditions impossible and divisions ran very deep.

Professor Anderson's team, which included Dr Neil Ferguson and Dr Christl Donnelly, had been working on the use of computers to model human diseases such as AIDS, malaria and TB, but suddenly at the first outbreak of FMD they had switched their resources to this disease. By one of those strange quirks of precognition that seem to surround this crisis, Dr Donnelly had out of the blue produced a paper on this disease of animals, when all their previous work had concerned humans. By applying their models to the earlier outbreak they had come to the conclusion that the only solution was the slaughter of all animals on the day of diagnosis. However, they now went further than that. Not only were they calling for the killing of all infected animals, but they also insisted that all animals should be killed in a contiguous zone of three kilometres, which was adopted by MAFF. Anderson had the considerable advantage of being pally with the pillars of the Government scientific establishment, Sir John Krebs, chief executive of the new Food Standards Agency, Professor David King, a chemist who was the new Government Chief Scientist and Sir Robert May, the former Chief Scientist and President of the Royal Society.

It is relevant at this point to comment on the touching faith that politicians and the media have in computer models. It is generally true to say that most large computer models are not worth the magnetic oxide they are written on, and I say that as one who has been computer modelling for well over 40 years. Often they are written in the glaring absence of knowledge of the fundamental interactions on which they ought to depend. A notorious case is the climate models that predicted catastrophic global warming, when almost nothing was known about the mechanisms that control the climate. In the case of FMD, they did not even know how the disease was carried. It could be on the wind, on the wheels of vehicles or the soles of boots, in the throats of human beings or any combination of these and others.

Computer modelling has a number of attractions for academics. It does not need the resources that experimental science demands; nor does it need the long hours of careful attention required for research by measurement. In just a few hours you can create a model, just a computer program, which is so complex that no outsider can hope to unravel it. You can build in many assumptions that might well be unjustifiable under independent examination. Furthermore, the human unconscious is a mischievous influence that can produce the desired results, even for those who are not deliberately cheating. In the same few hours you can produce beautiful graphs and tables, the like of which would take months in experimental science, but which are so convincing to laymen and particularly politicians and bureaucrats. This is a point so important that it is worth an interlude of its own.

An aside on computer modelling

> *A theory has only the alternative of being right or wrong. A model has a third possibility; it may be right, but irrelevant.*
> *Manfred Egan*

This is one of the most powerful tools available to science and engineering and, like all powerful tools, it brings dangers as well as benefits. Andrew Donald Booth said "Every system is its own best analogue". As a scientist he should, of course, have said in what sense he means best. The statement is true in terms of accuracy but not in terms of utility. If you want to determine the optimum shape for the members of a bridge structure, for example, you cannot build half a dozen bridges and test them to destruction, but you can try large numbers of variations in a computer model. Computers allow us to optimise designs in ways that were unavailable in times past. Nevertheless, the very flexibility of a computer program, the ease with which a glib algorithm can be implemented with a few lines of code and the difficulty of fully understanding its implications can pave the path to Cloud Cuckoo Land.

The main hazards of computer modelling can be summarised under a few headings:

Assumptions
At almost every stage in the development of a model it is necessary to make assumptions, perhaps hundreds of them. These might or might not be considered reasonable by others in the field, but they rapidly become hidden. Some of the larger models of recent times deal with the interactions of variables whose very nature is virtually unknown to science.

Auditability

In olden times, if a scientist published a theory, all the stages of reasoning that led to it could be critically examined by other scientists. With a computer model, it is possible, within a few days of development, for it to become so complex that it is a virtual impossibility for an outsider to understand it fully. Indeed, where it is the result of a team effort, it becomes unlikely that any individual understands it.

Omissions

Often vital elements can be left out of a model and the effect of the omissions is only realised if and when it is tested against reality. A notorious example is the Millennium Bridge in London. It was only after it was built and people started to walk on it that the engineers realised that they had created a resonant structure. This could have been modelled dynamically if they had thought about it. Now bridges are nothing new; they have been built for ages, and most of their characteristics are well known. There was even an example of the genre in the Tacoma Narrows suspension bridge in Puget Sound, Washington, which due to resonant behaviour self destructed under rather windy conditions in 1940. Thereafter, better mathematical models for bridge oscillation were developed. Some models that produce profound political and economic consequences have never faced such a challenge.

Subconscious

The human subconscious is a powerful force. Even in relatively simple physical measurements it has been shown that the results can be affected by the desires and expectations of the experimenter. In a large computer model this effect can be multiplied a thousand fold. Naturally, we discount the possibility of deliberate fraud.

Sophistication

This word, which literally means falsification or adulteration, has come to mean advanced and efficient. In large computer models, however, the literal meaning is often more applicable. The structure simply becomes too large and complex for the inputs that support it.

Testability

When we were pioneering the applications of computer modelling about forty years ago, we soon came to the conclusion that a model is useless unless it can be tested against reality. If a model gives a reasonably accurate prediction on a simple system then we have reasonable, but not irrefutable, grounds for believing it to be accurate in other circumstances. Unfortunately, this is one of the truisms that have been lost in the enthusiasms of the new age.

Chaos

Large models are often chaotic, which means that very small changes in the input variables produce very large changes in the output variables. Some very simple processes can amplify errors, taking the difference between numbers of a similar magnitude for example. The errors (or noise) are then propagated through the system. If there are feedback mechanisms present, it is quite possible for systems to operate on the noise alone.

Many of the computer models that receive great media coverage and political endorsement fail under some of these headings; and, indeed, some fail under all of them. Yet they are used as the excuse for profound, and often extremely damaging, policies that affect everyone.

That is why computer models are dangerous tools.

Back to the plot

One of the political developments that had occurred in the years leading up to the FMD crisis had been the inexorable move towards a presidential style of government. The Prime Minister, with his plans to hold an election before the economic bubble burst, himself took charge of the whole shooting match. Taking charge meant, of course, nominating individuals to do it for him. On the 22nd of March he paid a flying visit to Cumbria and was visibly shocked to meet a hail of abuse.

The result was nothing less than a complete coup. MAFF was swept aside, not only its incompetent bureaucrats but also its vets, who were the only people who had any expertise in the disease. The two men put in charge were Professor King, a surface chemist, and Professor Anderson, a computer programming human epidemiologist. It is difficult to imagine a more extraordinary choice of expertise on which to base a strategy.

By this time the dismal failure of the MAFF approach was underlined by the almost exponential rise in case numbers, to 846 by the end of the month. Anderson's computer was now in charge. Unfortunately, in addition to the inadequacies of the program itself, in the long tradition of GIGO (garbage in, garbage out) the data being fed into it were hopelessly wrong. Even the start date for the outbreak of February was probably wrong, but the reporting of cases was a disaster. The cull itself was destroying the evidence of the rate of infection.

Meanwhile an outbreak occurred in Holland. The Dutch implemented an immediate programme of vaccination, which suppressed the disease almost at once. The vaccinated animals were all slaughtered, but that was only done to satisfy the EU and its fears about its meat trading status. In Britain, the carnage, which had already seemed unimaginably barbaric, was about to enter an even more cataclysmic stage. The professor's computer, like some latter day insatiable Moloch, demanded more and more blood sacrifices. The hit squads, by now not only officials but also the army, were roaming the countryside shooting, bludgeoning and drowning perfectly healthy animals.

The anecdotes from this period read like a lunatic's account of a madman's war. A mistake in a map grid reference caused the deaths, not only of a farmer's livestock, but also his children's pets. Other stock were killed through clerical error. 20,000 animals in Devon were saved at the last minute when a mistaken diagnosis was discovered. Pregnant sheep were shot at random while they climbed over the corpses of their fellows. Houses were broken into so that pets could be slaughtered. Mounds of carcases lay neglected and rotting in the fields, others were transported in lorries through hitherto unaffected areas with blood dripping onto the roads. Funeral pyres sent clouds of reeking smoke across housing estates. Burial pits containing up to half a million corpses leached blood and gore into water supplies. Thousands had to be dug up again.

It was at this point, towards the end of April, that Prof King announced that the disease was "totally under control". The election, which had now been put off to June, was uppermost in political minds and the spin-doctors took over. Suddenly the slaughter of healthy cattle was not so important and sheep were put in the firing line as the main spreaders of the virus. This had the other considerable political advantage that the EU had decreed that Britain was overpopulated with sheep anyway. From now on, it would be presentation that mattered. By now the total number of outbreaks had risen to 1,517. MAFF began to present only daily figures and wiped all the historical data off its web site. Slaughterings were reclassified so that they did not appear in the daily headline figure. Outbreaks were only included when they had been confirmed by subsequent testing. Farmers in Cumbria claimed that 24 outbreaks in their area had been reported by MAFF as only 9. Most sinister of all was a sudden conversion by MAFF vets from a tendency to label every suspicious case as FMD to a reluctance to admit that even the most obvious cases were the disease at all.

Dr Paul Kitchen, Britain's leading expert on the disease, had been the most vehement critic of Prof Anderson's computer. In the face of the way the election date had been changed, with the computer predictions following conveniently, he resigned his post as deputy head of Pirbright and took up a post in Canada.

In May, as the election campaign warmed up, the situation became really weird. The media, and particularly the BBC, were lulled into a remarkable quietude by the presentation skills of the spin-doctors. They behaved as if the crisis were all but over. Out in the real world of the British countryside the slaughter had entered a new crescendo. The daily average of animals killed reached a startling 32,000. The total number of deaths was now 6 million, nearly a tenth of Britain's entire livestock. Ministers decreed the opening up of the countryside with photo-opportunities at appropriate tourist sites. Meanwhile, in places like Devon, Cumbria and Dumfries, the terror was being inflicted with greater intensity than ever. A few horror stories about armed gangs breaking in to slaughter pets leaked into the media. Farmers and animal sanctuary proprietors had begun legal challenges, many of which MAFF gave up on without a fight, by now being well aware that its actions had been quite illegal.

When another outbreak occurred in a new area, Settle in Yorkshire, MAFF suddenly refused to put the figures on its web site, citing the Data Protection Act as a reason. Secret mass burials were being carried out at the dead of night in ordinary landfill sites. Death squads of MAFF officials, backed up by dozens of policemen in riot gear, roamed the villages of Devon shooting every animal in sight. It was one of the most extraordinary examples of mass law-breaking in history, and all carried out be Government officials.

Tony Blair won his great gamble. Like his predecessor in large majority government, Margaret Thatcher, he was returned to power not by public enthusiasm for his own policies, but rather by the suicidal tendencies in the opposition. The aftermath was just as sordid as the conduct of the crisis itself. No official was punished for the massive breaches of the law. The only recognition that they had occurred was the Government's seeking powers to slaughter more legally in future. Calls from many influential sources for a full inquiry were ignored and the Government spin-doctors dreamed up a scheme of three innocuous mini-inquiries as a substitute. MAFF had its name changed to DEFRA, but they were the same people in the same offices with the same mind set. In the week after the election 80,000 animals were killed and in the following week 93,000. The government also began to speak of restricting farming to those with licences to carry it out.

The epidemiologists had the last word. Prof Anderson claimed in an article in *Nature* that one million animals and four hundred farms could have been saved if his cull policy had been "fully enforced". Even more bizarrely, Prof King stated in a TV interview that next time "vaccination would have to be top of the agenda", not explaining why next time would be different from the last. Nearly eight million animals, one eighth of all those in Britain and most of them healthy, had been slain. Mass bankruptcies occurred throughout the rural economy. Industries ranging from hotel chains to hot air balloon manufacturers were devastated. The total cost to the British economy was in the range 10 to 20 billion pounds. Promises of Government aid faded away in the miasma of bureaucratic manoeuvring and EU regulation.

And, as occurred in Holland, it could all have been avoided with a simple programme of vaccination. It was all done in the name of a theoretical disease free status, which had ironically been invented by the British. Above all, it was yet another triumph for the science of epidemiology. If you think such an ironic remark unduly provocative, consider the summing up a year later by Professor David King, the UK Government Chief Scientific Adviser, who described the handling of the foot-and-mouth epidemic as "quite an achievement . . . a magnificent record". He told the BBC Today programme that securing Britain's status as an FMD-free country was a cause for "celebration". Members of the European Parliament, among others, took rather a different view.

Anyway, the good professor surfaced again in January 2004. **US global warming delay worse that al Qaeda** bawled *The Times* headline. *The Telegraph* more modestly appended the story to a fantasy about early spring:

> *Tony Blair's chief scientific adviser says that climate change is a more serious threat than terrorism.*
>
> *In Science magazine today, Sir David King accuses America of failing to take global warming seriously. As a consequence of the phenomenon, he says, "millions more people around the world* **may** *in future be exposed to the risk of hunger, drought, flooding and diseases such as malaria".*

Now the reader might well be of that religious persuasion that adheres to the man-made global warming myth, but it depends on computer models with all the flaws that we have described above, yet are orders of magnitude larger that the ones responsible for the holocaust. Furthermore, previous warm periods have been times of the burgeoning of civilisation and culture, the disappearance of famine and the rise of prosperity. Also, as we observed way back in chapter 2, malaria is not just a tropical disease. To compare that with the threat from an evil bunch of mass murderers indicates a somewhat strange system of priorities, the sort that leads to the deaths of millions of innocent animals. Shortly after the Madrid railway bombings took place.

But enough of horror stories. Let us look at some other wonders.

16. Electromagnetic wonders

Across the wires the electric message came:
He is no better, he is much the same.
Alfred Austin (attributed)

Two typical stories appeared in the broadsheets during the last weekend in November 2003. This from the *Times* Business Section:

Idea of the week: Anti-static watches offer timely opportunity

MADONNA wears one and wants to order tiny ones for her kids. Rap artist Sean 'P Diddy' Combs has the diamond model.

Celebrities are scrambling to buy the latest health/fashion craze in the US — a watch with a chip that is said to protect against electronic pollution from mobile phones, computers and DVD players.

The watch, made by Philip Stein, is flying off the shelves at stores such as Bloomingdale's and Saks in America, where customers are paying nearly $600 (£350) for a basic model, and upwards of $1,995 for a diamond-encrusted style.

It was developed by Ilonka Harezi, a researcher who has been studying the effect of electromagnetic frequencies (EMFs) on the human body.

While this one was featured prominently in the *Daily Telegraph*:

Protesters topple mobile phone masts as health scare spreads

Activists have begun tearing down mobile-phone masts around the country, as public concern over the health impact of the radiation they emit continues to grow.

The destruction of the masts - as many as four in a single week - signals a dramatic stepping up of the campaign to stop them being placed on top of, or close to, people's houses.

Earlier this month, masts were brought down at Wishaw and Dudley in the West Midlands, Crosby in Merseyside and Tiverton in Devon. At least four have also been brought down in Northern Ireland in recent months.

It is difficult to convey just how absurd such stories are to anyone who has made even the most cursory study of electromagnetic fields. There are two possible physiological effects that such fields can have on the human body. There is the heating effect, such as is used in diathermy for the treatment of injuries, and there are quantum effects. For heating effects, the field strengths are too low by at least a million times. Quantum effects depend on the quantum of energy available, which is proportional to frequency. Visible light, for example, can produce chemical changes, as in photography or photosynthesis, but for radio frequencies the quantum of energy is far lower. The energy that comes with a packet of visible light (known as a photon) is a few electron-volts, the equivalent photon energy of a high frequency radio wave is a million times smaller. Any effect such fields have on the human body emanates from the wilder fantasies of epidemiologists, as we saw in our exercise of chapter 9.

Electromagnetism provides a wonderful playground for scaremongers and miracle cure salesmen. Electric and magnetic fields are invisible, yet we can observe their effects. There are not only the static fields but also the spectrum of electromagnetic waves from mains frequencies to gamma rays via radio, microwaves, infrared, visible light, ultra violet and X-rays. The higher frequencies have ionising properties, which means that they can disrupt atoms and molecules, including those within the human body; in all a veritable feast of effects, both real and imaginary.

Besides the fact that the magnitudes are far too small, there is the question of the way electromagnetic fields distribute themselves. It is governed by a set of mathematical equations derived by Maxwell. The fields spread through space and the idea that any device at one point in space, such as a watch or the crystals famously worn in necklaces sported by the wives of political leaders in Britain and America, can neutralise them is preposterous.

It is remarkable how even so-called experts can be led astray by ideas of electromagnetic fields.

N-Rays
This account is condensed from the highly recommended Skeptic's Dictionary web site by Robert Todd Carroll:

> René Prosper Blondlot (1849-1930) was a French physicist who claimed to have discovered a new type of radiation, shortly after Roentgen had discovered X-rays. He called it the N-ray, after Nancy, the name of the town and the university where he lived and worked. Dozens of other scientists confirmed the existence of N-rays in their own laboratories. However, N-rays don't exist. How could so many scientists be wrong? They deceived themselves into thinking they were seeing something when in fact they were not. They saw what they wanted to see with their instruments, not what was actually there (or, in this case, what was not there).

> Blondlot claimed that N-rays exhibit impossible properties and yet are emitted by all substances except green wood and certain treated metals. In 1903, Blondlot claimed he had generated N-rays using a hot wire inside an iron tube. The rays were detected by a calcium sulfide thread that glowed slightly in the dark when the rays were refracted through a 60-degree angle prism of aluminum. According to Blondlot, a narrow stream of N-rays was refracted through the prism and produced a spectrum on a field. The N-rays

were reported to be invisible, except when viewed as they hit the treated thread. Blondlot moved the thread across the gap where the N-rays were thought to come through and when the thread was illuminated it was said to be due to N-rays.

Nature magazine was skeptical of Blondlot's claims because laboratories in England and Germany had not been able to replicate the Frenchman's results. Nature sent American physicist Robert W. Wood of Johns Hopkins University to investigate Blondlot's discovery. Wood suspected that N-rays were a delusion. To demonstrate such, he removed the prism from the N-ray detection device, unbeknownst to Blondlot or his assistant. Without the prism, the machine couldn't work. Yet, when Blondlot's assistant conducted the next experiment he found N-rays. Wood then tried to surreptitiously replace the prism but the assistant saw him and thought he was removing the prism. The next time he tried the experiment, the assistant swore he could not see any N-rays. But he should have, since the equipment was in full working order.

Carrol adds

The story of Blondlot is a story of self-deception among scientists. Because many people have the misguided notion that science should be infallible and a fount of absolutely certain truths, they look at the Blondlot episode as a vindication of their excessive skepticism towards science. They relish accounts such as the one regarding Blondlot and the phantom N-rays because it is a story of a famous scientist making a great error. However, if one properly understands science and scientists, the Blondlot episode indicates little more than the fallibility of scientists and the self-correcting nature of science.

All true, but one might question whether the self-correcting nature of science is shared by epidemiology.

The light fantastic
Here is a story from *The Times*, July 2000:

Red and blue light may help to eliminate acne, a dermatologist believes.

The method, developed at Hammersmith Hospital in West London, involves regular sessions with blue and red light rather than traditional treatments such as antibiotics.

Trials by Dr Tony Chu, a consultant dermatologist at the hospital, published in the British Journal of Dermatology, showed a 76 per cent decrease in the number of visible spots in 12 weeks.

Mild to moderate forms of acne are often treated by antibiotics, which can take months to work. Ultraviolet radiation in natural sunlight is also known to help clear acne but at some risk of skin damage.

Dr Chu has found that blue and red lights, at higher wavelengths than ultraviolet, can be very effective. In trials, patients were sent home with portable lights and used them for 15 minutes a day.

Dr Chu believes that the blue light kills the bacteria in the skin that cause acne while the red seems to help the healing process.

"Importantly, they do this without any significant side-effects," he said.

Poor old Sir Isaac. Early in the Twentieth century that revisionist Albert Einstein was tinkering with his laws of motion. Now in the Twenty First, another genius is rubbishing his great work *Opticks*, in which he demonstrated that white light from the sun contains all wavelengths, including red and blue. But these days, my dear, physics is so passé.

Three years later he was back, and on the front page of the *Daily Telegraph*. He had abandoned ordinary light and now used the **Nlite** laser. The *Trojan Number* was a little disappointing, at 41, but he did admit that **more research is needed**. Ah, that strain again!

Rather an unfortunate name for the magic laser, as it is redolent of M Blondlot and his N-rays. Following the links we find that Nlite emits a gentle yellow light. The science is the same, only the colour has been changed to protect the innocent.

Pylons

In order to establish a leading reputation among the scare mongers it is necessary to specialise. **Pylon man** is Professor Henshaw, a physicist at Bristol University. This from the BBC in December 1999:

People living and working near high voltage electricity cables may face a greater danger of getting cancer than those who do not, controversial research has concluded.

After completing 2,000 experiments near pylons, a team from the University of Bristol has concluded the cables are responsible for trebling the amount of cancer-carrying pollutants in the air.

Professor Denis Henshaw and his team said the electromagnetic field surrounding the cables was to blame for the alleged link between power lines and childhood leukaemia.

But you can't keep the old favourites out:

The other study - a wide-ranging analysis of childhood cancers in the UK by respected scientist Sir Richard Doll - is due to be published in the Lancet medical journal on Friday - and will be the strongest indicator yet of whether or not a link exists.

Once you have established your speciality you are then poised to jump on any passing bandwagon. This from *The Independent* June 2001:

One of the world's leading experts on the effects of radiation believes electricity pylons have helped spread foot and mouth disease.

David Henshaw, a professor of physics at Bristol University, says the high-voltage power lines make the virus even more virulent. He believes the virus, carried by the wind, is electrically charged by the power lines and so better able to "stick" to animals. The principle works in much the same way as static electricity – just as a statically charged balloon sticks to clothing, so the statically charged foot and mouth virus adheres to animals.

The prospect of pylons helping to spread foot and mouth is alarming. But it could explain why the disease was so easily spread – via super-charged, wind-born particles of the virus – and so hard to contain. "Powerlines could well be an important contributory factor in the spread of foot and mouth," said Professor Henshaw, who specialises in the effects of powerline radiation on humans.

It is a strange phenomenon that some professors, once they get a taste of media coverage, develop a headline hunger that dominates everything they do. You see the same few names over and over again. In order to generate the sort of stuff the media love to wallow in, they move further towards the fringe of real science and, almost inevitably, go beyond the fringe. They also manoeuvre themselves on to national committees that cover the sorts of areas that excite media comment.

Two of the established British media heroes, Richard Doll and Colin Blakemore, got themselves onto the Advisory Group on Non-Ionising Radiation (AGNIR) of the National Radiological Protection Board (NRPB), though their qualifications for being there seemed somewhat obscure. Lo and behold, in March 2001, this group came up with a typical empty scare story about power lines and leukaemia, which to the joy of the media could be labelled "official". The parent body in its response was somewhat less than enthusiastic, though it ended up with the classic formula that more epidemiological research was needed. Why don't they just set fire to a pile of taxpayers' money, achieving the same effect with little effort? The odd thing is that what they are discussing has nothing at all to do with radiation; so the whole nonsense is beyond the remit of this particular board anyway. Here are some of the comments I made in an article for *Spiked* in the same month:

The report claims that the overall risk of leukaemia, which in all children is 1 in 1400, becomes elevated to 1 in 700 for those exposed to magnetic fields of 0.4microTesla or more (about 0.5 percent of children). This is a risk ratio of 2, which is considered unacceptable in all branches of science except epidemiology. In actual numbers, however, it represents about one extra case of leukaemia every two years as a result of exposure to magnetic fields – this, out of a total number of 500 cases per year.

Even if such a phenomenon were to exist, it would generally be considered to be undetectable by available statistical methods. There are many other questions that occur: for example, why 0.4microTesla? How much exposure and for how long? What other phenomena correlate with power lines? (For example, do rich people live under them?) These questions, however, are dwarfed by the minuscule nature of the numbers involved.

Here are one or two facts that might be worth considering:

1. The radiation at mains frequency is infinitesimal. What they are dealing with at such slow rates of change are effectively electrostatic and magnetostatic fields, which depend on the voltage and current respectively, unlike true radiation where the electric and magnetic fields are inextricably bound together by Maxwell's equations. It is possible to radiate efficiently at such frequencies, but you would need an antenna a thousand miles long.
2. Magnetic fields do not cause ionisation, only electric fields do, especially at sharp points or when the air is damp, when an electric breakdown phenomenon called corona occurs (which is why your AM radio crackles when you go under power lines in wet weather).
3. Because the voltages and currents are alternating and the phases balance, nearly all effects from power lines decrease extremely rapidly with distance from them. This includes magnetic and electric field strength and net ion charge. However, corona does produce in small quantities somewhat toxic gases such as ozone and the oxides of nitrogen, which in most areas would be lost in the prevailing pollution.
4. The only evidence offered by this group is epidemiological, i.e. very weak statistical associations based on cluster watching.

Just to establish his headline-hunting credentials Colin Blakemore made the front page of *The Times* again on March 14. This time it was on the basis that he had written to the leadership of the Conservative party expressing his dismay at the party's policy on animal experiments. Now many people write to the leadership of the Conservative party, including this author, but they do not call in the journos as well. It reminds one of the piece of dialogue in the film Arthur:

Arthur: Do you know what I'm going to do? I'm going to take a bath.

Hobson: I'll alert the media.

Mobiles

Nothing is certain in human affairs, they say, but it was inevitable that the most popular technical innovation in history would come under attack from fame-seeking epidemiologists; and, if epidemiologists come, can American personal injury lawyers be far behind? Mobile phones (also known as cell phones or hand phones), discounting the period when they were like bricks, were in use by over half the population in most advanced economies within a decade. First, let us establish the fundamental absurdity of the idea that they are harmful. Most of the population are involved in the biggest epidemiological trial ever. If there were a tiny annual probability (say 0.0001) that the devices caused, say toe-nail cancer, there would be 4,000 new cases every year, enough to swamp the relevant hospital wards. It has not happened. Such a probability is way below the detectable level by "normal" epidemiological methods, but by this stage we know that this is not going to deter our heroes. So in January 2002 it was announced, in defiance of all logic and commonsense, that Britain was going to spend £7.4 million on examining the health risks of mobile phones. Rarely, even in the recent history of the post-scientific age, can there have been such an absurd project.

However, let's not let logic get in the way of the PR of the professors of doom. Nor do we need any whingeing about the money being diverted from trimming 2,000 off the waiting list for operations or funding 50 alpha-rated genuine research projects that have been turned down. This is the 21st century, dammit!

The Times had to be pulling our legs! They announced on February 5th 2001 that Roger Coghill has been invited to sit on a Government panel to monitor the safety of mobile phone technology. *The Times* also told us that Dr Coghill, an independent scientist who runs Coghill Research Laboratories in South Wales, is an **expert in bioelectromagnetics**, the study of the effects of electromagnetic radiation on living tissue. His web site offers all sorts of electromagnetic wonders, even for your horse or dog, including a **magnetic coaster** for only twenty pounds sterling:

> *About the size of a CD, this powerful coaster has powerful magnets hidden within an attractive wipe clean plastic shell. Use it to 'magnetise' drinking water, or even improve the taste of red wine (!) Every kitchen should have at least one.*

Here are some other delights:

Mood Maker
Price: £52.35 Pounds Sterling
Can help with impotency without the use of powerful drugs. The Mood Maker will gently and gradually increase circulation in the pelvic area. The small unit discreetly attaches to your underwear.

Pet Coaster
Price: £20.00 Pounds Sterling
Given the choice your pet will always choose to drink magnetic water, they can tell the difference. Magnetic water is more natural. Using a pet coaster ensures that your pet receives maximum benefit from their drinking water. They will love the taste.

Harmoniser
Price: £17.62 Pounds Sterling
Promotes that feeling of wellbeing and gain personal protection from most RF radiations with this pendant device. Also available in Silver and Gold.

Anyway, among all these wonders is a book called *Masts and Mobiles* in which you can "Find out if there is a risk from mobile phones and the base stations which seem to be everywhere today." *The Times* in January 2001 carried this story, which typified the genre

Mobile may have 'caused tumour'
By David Charter Health Correspondent
A TUMOUR removed from the head of a former telephone engineer could have been caused by mobile phone use, his surgeon said yesterday.

Michael Edwards, a surgeon at the Friarage Hospital in Northallerton, North Yorkshire, called on other doctors to look out for growths in the saliva glands of frequent mobile phone users.

Mr Edwards reported the non-malignant tumour in the current issue of Laryngology and Otology. He found that there had been only 21 similar tumours reported worldwide.

His report came just days after The Times disclosed that Vodafone would be sued in America by up to ten brain tumour victims who had used mobiles. The Government announced a £7 million research programme last month to try to establish once and for all whether there were long-term health risks. An earlier inquiry by Sir William Stewart, published in May, found no clear danger, but recommended a precautionary approach to their use, particularly among children.

Mr Edwards, who removed the growth from the unnamed 39-year-old patient, said: "I had never seen a growth like it before. We had to go in through the mouth to reach it. It was attached to the salivary gland. The patient told us that he was using the mobile phone against the same ear for an hour a day for four years.

Here are a few of the headlines from the *Daily Telegraph*, the least hysterical of our newspapers;

24 May 2001: **Sending text messages may damage your health**
8 February 2001: **Mobile phone use carries no cancer risk, says study**
18 January 2001: **County council poised to ban mobile phone masts**
12 May 2000: **Health risks for children will be investigated**
11 May 2000: **Mobile phone firms vow to allay child health fears**

Not a bad haul from a statistical sample of one. Of course, when danger threatens there are always noble souls who will come up with preventatives. The BBC in October 2001 offered Aulterra

> *Aulterra is an organic compound from a crystalline rock found by Mr Dandurand in 1995.*
>
> *He found that the substance reacted with the earth's magnetic fields and neutralised radiation from soils.*
>
> *He told BBC Radio Scotland's Good Morning Scotland programme that the sticker would offer mobile phone users the opportunity of a safeguard if they saw fit.*
>
> *"The easiest way to describe it is that it neutralises any damaging effect from electro magnetic waves from a cellphone on human DNA," Mr Dandurand said.*
>
> *"That is what it does. How it works is that it allows the wave to become more coherent or more like a laser beam and less like a flashlight and more of a focus coming from your cellphone.*
>
> *"Therefore it does not damage the biological system as it goes through it.*
>
> *If you put the sticker on the mobile phone then the DNA recovers 100% every time you carry out the experiment.*

Let us leave the last word to James Le Fanu, one of the few cool heads in the interlinked worlds of journalism and medicine:

> *Then there is bed rest. Dr Richard Asher, in an article in The Lancet, "The dangers of going to bed", highlighted the hazards. "Look at the person lying in bed; what a pathetic picture he makes," he wrote, "the blood clotting in his veins, the calcium draining from his bones, the flesh rotting on his buttocks and the spirit evaporating from his soul." And the interesting point about all these health hazards is that they are*

based on considerably more substantiating evidence than the allegation which surfaced again this week that mobile phones can damage the brain.

Yet all mobile phones sold in Britain will soon carry health warnings about the dangers of excess use.

This way lies madness. Why not be done with it and just attach a health warning to everything - goalposts, toothbrushes and bed rest included?

Mobile phones transmit radio frequencies of such low intensity that their biological effects can scarcely be detected; even the most high-powered devices raise the temperature of tissues in the immediate vicinity by less than 0.05°F. The question as to whether they may have any long-term adverse effect has been examined over 15 years in nearly 200,000 employees of Motorola.

The conclusion? You could buy a mobile tomorrow and use it continuously for 2.7 million years without fear that it might be doing you any harm.

And yet a blue-chip Government inquiry this year, chaired by Sir William Stewart, felt unable to assert that mobile phones were "harmless". This loss of nerve in the face of anxiety-mongering by the "consumer health watchdogs" is regrettable. It suggests, falsely, that scientific investigation cannot distinguish truth from falsehood. It heightens public neuroticism and deprives the few valid official health warnings of any force or meaning.

Genuine radiation

Sunburn and skin cancer

Mad dogs and Englishmen go out in the midday sun
Noel Coward

This book has taken a fairly cynical view of most health scares, and especially those based on marginal statistics. It is difficult to do so in the case of skin cancer and its purported relationship to sunburn. Of course, epidemiologists have tried to "link" the diseases to almost anything, including of course smoking, but as scientists we say "Where is the mechanism?" In the case of sunbathing the mechanism is only too apparent. Skin cancers have been increasing rapidly worldwide for many years and the rise is parallel to the increase in mass travel and tourism. The country most affected is Australia, where about three quarters of a million cases occur every year and nearly one half of the population will experience one of the diseases in a life time. Long standing natives of tropical countries have developed substantial immunity through the attrition of survival of the fittest, but the mass migration of fair skinned northern Europeans has subjected them to exposures to which they are not conditioned by evolution.

The spectrum of light contains frequencies from the infra-red to the ultra-violet. The lower frequency radiation can cause trauma to the skin simply by overheating it. Ultra-violet radiation, however, has a quantum energy in the region of tens of electron volts, which means that the photons have enough energy to disrupt the bonds in the many complex organic compounds that constitute the human skin, including DNA. The body has considerable powers to repair lesions in DNA, but that capacity might well be overwhelmed given a sufficient photon flux over sufficient time, so it is not just burning but addiction to tanning that is potentially harmful.

There are three classes of skin cancer. Basal cell carcinoma is relatively benign, slow growing and easily dealt with. Squamous cell carcinoma is rather more dangerous and can spread if not dealt with. The really dangerous form, however, is melanoma, which is malignant, invasive, quick growing and often lethal. Melanoma represents only 4% of skin cancers but it is the eighth most common cancer in the USA, causing about eight thousand fatalities.

The epidemiologists make their usual contribution in the form of periodic headlines "linking" sunscreen use to skin cancer. As usual they are confusing correlation with causation. The people who use sunscreen are the ones who have experienced sunburn and are therefore more vulnerable.

Ionising radiations

Above ultra-violet in the electromagnetic spectrum are soft X rays, hard X rays and Gamma rays. In addition there is particulate radiation – alpha particles, which are helium nuclei, and beta particles, electrons or positrons. They are all carriers of high-energy quanta that can disrupt the structure of matter. In the early days of radiation physics, the dangers were not appreciated and a total of 406 experimenters died, including Marie Sklodowska-Curie. The following comments are largely distilled from the essay by Zbigniew Jaworowski in *What Risk* (see Bibliography).

At the outset experimenters conceived of a "tolerance dose", i.e. a threshold of annual exposure to radiation below which there are no adverse effects. This started out at 700 mSv in modern SI units, and by 1941 was gradually whittled down to 70 mSv. This was a rational conception, which accorded with most biological stimulus-response phenomena. However, round about 1960 politics had entered the scene, mainly through the Byzantine workings of the United Nations, and the rational threshold model was gradually replaced by a no-threshold model.

It was like arguing that, because a temperature of 200°C produces third degree burns, a temperature of 20°C would be hazardous. This posed questions that science could not possibly answer. For example, it was calculated that to confirm the hazard at 1.5 mSv that the extrapolation predicted from high doses at the "usual" 95% confidence level, it would require the sacrifice of 8,000,000,000 mice. Many leading scientists in the field of radiation protection protested that the assumption was nonsense.

The madness reached its zenith in the response to the Chernobyl incident. 400,000 people were resettled, because of an exposure that was of the same order of magnitude as natural background radiation. The human suffering was immense. Why was not the entire population of Norway resettled? Their lifetime exposure to natural radiation is three times the limit set for the Chernobyl evacuation. In some districts of Iran the exposure is more than 20 times that limit.

But it is all even more absurd than that, because of the phenomenon of radiation *hormesis*. It has been known since 1898, shortly after the discovery of X rays, that small doses of radiation have beneficial effects on living organisms. In the Manhattan project in 1943, animals exposed to Uranium dust did not expire as expected but actually lived longer, appeared healthier and had more offspring than the control animals. Hormetic effects were there to be seen in the literature, even after the workings of *publication bias*, but authors simply ignored them. Jaworowski gives example after example. Just one of these is illustrated in Fig 16.1. It involves mice subjected to various doses of gamma radiation and shows the percentage of tumours plotted against radiation dose.

We could go on and on. Periodically estimates appear in the newspapers of the number of deaths from cancer due to hospital X-rays. They are, of course, based on the no-threshold supposition and ignoring the possibility of radiation hormesis. The most likely number of deaths from this cause is nil, but let us not allow that to stand in the way of a good scare.

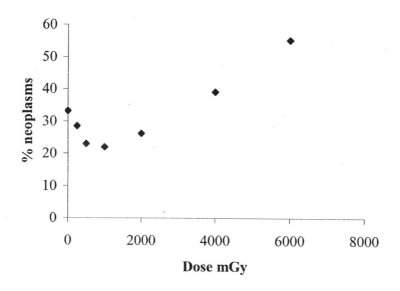

Figure 16.1 Number of tumours in mice versus radiation dose

So there it is, the world of electromagnetic wonders. It is populated by charlatans selling junk to mugs who have been frightened to death by so-called scientists peddling baseless scares. The demon haunted world of primitive man, which all but vanished during the brief flourish of the scientific age, has been restored since that age came to an end in the last quarter of the twentieth century. Mindless mobs tear down antennae that expose them to about one thousandth of the radiation dose that their own mobile phones do, just as their ancestors did in the Luddite machine-breaking riots. Pusillanimous "experts", mindful that their knighthoods might be in jeopardy, look on and bleat "More research is needed."

The US Nuclear Regulatory Commission's regulations cost that benighted nation about $2.5 billion per annum. If the well-established phenomenon of hormesis were taken into account, that expenditure would not only prove futile, it might actually be making the population less healthy. Britain spends £7.4 million on researching the hazards of mobile phones, when simple observation of the population tells you there aren't any. Celebrities, including the wives of political leaders, wear useless talismans to protect them against radiation hazards that exist only in their minds.

It's a mad world, my masters!

So, who are the major players in the scare game?

17. The Players

A fool's brain digests philosophy into folly, science into superstition, and art into pedantry. Hence University education.
George Bernard Shaw

Harvard

Harvard University, which celebrated its 350th anniversary in 1986, is the oldest institution of higher education in the United States. Harvard College was established in 1636 by vote of the Great and General Court of the Massachusetts Bay Colony and was named after its first benefactor, John Harvard of Charlestown, a young minister who, upon his death in 1638, left his library and half his estate to the new institution.

School of Public Health

Founded in 1922, the Harvard School of Public Health grew out of the Harvard-MIT School for Health Officers, America's first graduate training program in public health. In its first 50 years, the School was responsible for many landmark contributions to public health. Early accomplishments include the identification of the health effects of lead and other toxins, viral research that paved the way for the development of polio vaccines, and the invention of such lifesaving devices as the iron lung, which sustained the lives of many stricken with paralytic polio, and the cardiac defibrillator, now used widely in treating heart failure.

The School of Public Health, however, begat the Department of Epidemiology, which spawned –

Harvard Nurses' Health study

This was established in 1976. It was to become the biggest *data dredge* ever. Approximately 122,000 nurses out of the 170,000 mailed responded. Every two years cohort members received a follow-up questionnaire with questions about diseases and health-related topics including smoking, hormone use and menopausal status. In 1980, the first food frequency questionnaire was collected. Subsequent diet questionnaires were collected in 1984, 1986 and every four years since. The nurses submitted 68,000 sets of toenail samples between the 1982 and 1984 questionnaires. Similarly, to identify potential biomarkers, such as hormone levels and genetic markers, 33,000 blood samples were collected in 1989. These samples are stored and used in case/control analyses. A second blood collection from those who previously gave a sample was conducted in 2000/2001.

A second wave was established in 1989 to study oral contraceptives, diet and lifestyle risk factors in a population younger than the original Nurses' Health Study cohort. This younger generation included women who started using oral contraceptives during adolescence and were thus maximally exposed during their early reproductive life. The scale and influence of the nurses' study is staggering. It has produced 500 scientific publications and rising. Figure 17.1 shows the rate of growth of publications since its inception.

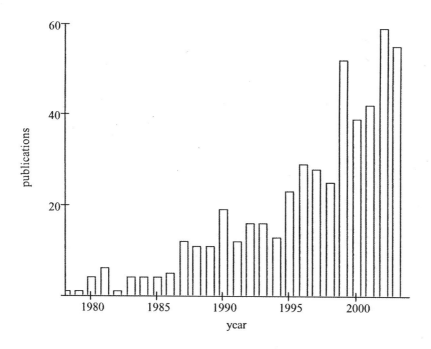

Figure 17.1 Number of publications each year from the Nurses' Health Study

Here is just a **small** selection of (condensed) titles from the canon:
Vitamin and carotenoid intake and risk of squamous cell carcinoma of the skin.
Vitamin D, milk consumption, and hip fractures: a prospective study among postmenopausal women.
Prospective study of sleep duration and coronary heart disease in women.
Prospective study of self-reported sleep duration and incident diabetes in women.
Meat, fish and egg intake and risk of breast cancer.
Major dietary patterns and the risk of colorectal cancer in women.
Total hip replacement due to osteoarthritis: the importance of age, obesity, and other modifiable risk factors.
Adolescent diet and risk of breast cancer.
Plasma folate, vitamin B6, vitamin B12, homocysteine, and risk of breast cancer.
High-dose antioxidant supplements and cognitive function in community-dwelling elderly women.
Caffeine, postmenopausal estrogen, and risk of Parkinson's disease.
Television watching and other sedentary behaviors in relation to risk of obesity and type 2 diabetes mellitus in women.
Fish and long-chain omega-3 fatty acid intake and risk of coronary heart disease and total mortality in diabetic women.
Can dietary fatty acids affect colon cancer risk?
Dietary carotenoids and risk of coronary artery disease in women.
Dietary meat, dairy products, fat, and cholesterol and pancreatic cancer risk.
Night-shift work and risk of colorectal cancer.
Alcohol consumption in relation to risk of cholecystectomy in women.

Vitamin C and risk of coronary heart disease in women.
Dietary intakes of fat and risk of Parkinson's disease.
Antioxidant Intake and the Risk of Primary Open-angle Glaucoma.
Premenopausal dietary carbohydrate, glycemic index, glycemic load, and fiber in relation to risk of breast cancer.
Influence on serum levels of insulin-like growth factors, interaction with plasma retinol and vitamin D, and breast cancer risk.
Joint association of alcohol and folate intake with risk of major chronic disease in women.
Caregiving to children and grandchildren and risk of coronary heart disease in women.
Changes in intakes of dietary fiber and grain products and changes in weight and development of obesity among middle-aged women.
Sex steroid hormone exposures and risk for meningioma.
A prospective study of plasma total cysteine and risk of breast cancer.
Body iron stores and its determinants in healthy postmenopausal US women.
Prospective study of cigarette smoking and the risk of primary open-angle glaucoma.
Alcohol consumption and the incidence of Parkinson's disease.
The association between magnesium intake and fasting insulin concentration in healthy middle-aged women.
Vitamin A intake and hip fractures among postmenopausal women.
Smoking cessation and risk of cataract extraction.
Active and passive smoking in breast cancer.
Snoring as a risk factor for type 2 diabetes mellitus.
Smoking and risk of coronary heart disease among women with type 2 diabetes mellitus.
Long-term intake of vitamins and carotenoids and odds of early age-related cortical and posterior subcapsular lens opacities.
The influence of folate and multivitamin use on the familial risk of colon cancer in women.
Calcium intake and risk of colon cancer in women and men.
Meat and dairy food consumption and breast cancer.
Dietary fat, fat subtypes, and breast cancer risk.
Fish and omega-3 fatty acid and risk of coronary heart disease in women.
Vitamins and carotenoids intake and the risk of basal cell carcinoma of the skin in women.
Monoamine oxidase B intron 13 and catecol-O-methyltransferase codon 158 polymorphisms, cigarette smoking, and the risk of Parkinson's disease.
Menstrual cycle irregularity and risk for future cardiovascular disease.
Dietary fat intake and ovarian cancer.
Obesity and risk of coronary heart disease among diabetic women.
Postmenopausal hormone use and lens opacities.
Endogenous sex hormones and breast cancer in postmenopausal women.
Breast cancer and breastfeeding.
Obesity, weight gain, and ovarian cancer.
Aspirin, other NSAIDS, and ovarian cancer.
Correlates of bone and blood lead levels among middle-aged and elderly women
Dietary sugar, glycemic load, and pancreatic cancer risk.
Intake of dairy products, calcium, and vitamin D and risk of breast cancer.
Dietary fat and risk of lung cancer.
Intake of alcohol and alcoholic beverages and the risk of basal cell carcinoma of the skin.
Intakes of vitamins E and C, carotenoids, vitamin supplements, and Parkinson's Disease risk.
Relationship between body mass index and cataract extraction.
Nonnarcotic analgesic use and the risk of hypertension in US women.
Walking and leisure-time activity and risk of hip fracture in postmenopausal women.
Supplemental vitamin E intake and risk of colon cancer in women and men.
Intake of dairy products, calcium, and vitamin D and risk of breast cancer.

Use of postmenopausal hormones, alcohol, and risk for invasive breast cancer.
Diet quality and major chronic disease risk in men and women: Moving toward improved dietary guidance.
Nut and peanut butter consumption and risk of type 2 diabetes in women.
Coffee intake is associated with lower risk of symptomatic gallstone disease in women.
Polychlorinated biphenyls, cytochrome, and breast cancer risk.
A prospective study of job strain and coronary heart disease in US women.
Diet and Parkinson's disease: a potential role of dairy products in men.
Dietary fat and the risk of age-related macular degeneration.
Intake of fruits and vegetables and risk of breast cancer.
Plasma organochlorine levels and the risk of breast cancer.
Intake of fish and omega-3 fatty acids and risk of stroke in women.
Physical activity and risk for cardiovascular events in diabetic women.
Prospective study of fat and protein intake and risk of intraparenchymal hemorrhage in women.
Genetic variation in alcohol dehydrogenase and the beneficial effect of moderate alcohol consumption on myocardial infarction.
Association of bowel movement frequency and use of laxatives with the occurrence of symptomatic gallstone disease.
Physical activity and mortality.
Prospective study of cataract extraction and risk of coronary heart disease in women.
Ethylene and polychlorinated biphenyls and breast cancer.
Coffee and alcohol consumption and the risk of pancreatic cancer.
Types of dietary fat and breast cancer.
Dietary fat intake and risk of Type 2 diabetes in women.
Vitamin supplement use and the risk of non-Hodgkin's lymphoma among women and men.
Prospective study of zinc intake and the risk of age-related macular degeneration.
Prospective study of recreational physical activity and ovarian cancer.
The effect of fruit and vegetable intake on risk for coronary heart disease.
Postmenopausal hormone use and secondary prevention of coronary events.
Impact of overweight on the risk of developing common chronic diseases during a 10-year period.
Prospective study of caffeine consumption and risk of Parkinson's disease in men and women.
Long-term nutrient intake and early age-related nuclear lens opacities.
Dietary patterns and the risk of coronary heart disease in women.
Diet, lifestyle, and the risk of type 2 diabetes mellitus in women.
Rotating night shifts and risk of breast cancer.
Physical activity, obesity, height, and the risk of pancreatic cancer.
Risk of ovarian carcinoma and consumption of vitamins A, C, and E and specific carotenoids.
Smoking and mortality among women with type 2 diabetes.
Cigarette smoking and the incidence of Parkinson's disease.
Prospective study of talc use and ovarian cancer.
Snoring and risk of cardiovascular disease in women.
Prospective study of alcohol consumption and the risk of age-related macular degeneration.
Intakes of fruits, vegetables, and related nutrients and the risk of non-Hodgkin's lymphoma among women.

What this tells us is that there are several dozen different diseases that were covered in the dredge and even more potential causes. This means that the combined matrix of possible relationships has thousands of entries. Entering them into the one-in-twenty lottery that is the normal standard of significance in modern epidemiology means that you are **guaranteed** hundreds of apparently significant associations, particularly if you are not too choosy about the *relative risks* you are prepared to accept. Yet, in the publications, the probabilities for each random association are calculated as though they were individual trials, which is mathematically quite inadmissible and the essential feature of the data dredge illusion.

It would be difficult to overstate the effect that the Nurses' Study has had on modern life. Most of the dietary advice given by contemporary gurus can be traced back to it. It has set the standard for lesser departments of epidemiology. It has spawned draconian legislation and civil law suits for billions of dollars. The proponents campaign ceaselessly for the diversion of precious research funds from the fundamental study of cancer, which is most likely to provide a solution, to claimed prevention programmes. The mind-set of such people is not easy to understand. Do they really believe that eating eggs during adolescence reduces the probability of getting breast cancer, while eating butter increases it?

Yale

Harvard's ancient rival seems to have avoided some of the excesses we have seen above. It is no coincidence that the critical comment in our exercise of Chapter 9 came from a Yale epidemiologist. Such differences in cultural development often boil down to one or two personalities. Harvard had the likes of John Bailar III, while Yale had Alvan Feinstein.

If you want to see an elegant, rigorous and scientific explanation of what has gone wrong in much of modern epidemiology, read Feinstein's essay in *What Risk* (see bibliography) entitled *Biases introduced by confounding and imperfect retrospective and prospective exposure assessments*. It represents a return to the rigour originally bequeathed by the likes of Fisher and Hill. Ironically, Feinstein came under the same *ad hominem* attack as had Fisher, that he had done work for the dreaded tobacco industry. His assessment that the evidence against passive smoking was "inadequate" was a masterpiece of understatement and based on sound science, yet he was harangued by the medical establishment not on the basis of what he said but of who he was.

The above is what I originally drafted about Yale and then this happened:

> *For Immediate Release: January 23, 2004*
> ### *Hair Dye Use Increases Risk of Non-Hodgkin's Lymphoma*
> *New Haven, Conn. -- Yale researchers have found that lifetime users of hair coloring products have an increased risk of developing non-Hodgkin's lymphoma (NHL), a cancer that attacks the lymphatic system, part of the body's immune system.......*
>
> *The six-year study was conducted on 601 Connecticut women diagnosed with varying subtypes of NHL between the ages of 21 and 84. The women were asked to identify the type of hair coloring products they had ever used, length of time used, and their age when they stopped using it. The study included a control group of 717 women.*

Then this

Cigarette smoking and risk of non-Hodgkin lymphoma subtypes among women

Compared with nonsmokers, women with a cumulative lifetime exposure of 16-33 pack-years and 34 pack-years or greater experience 50% increased risk (OR=1.5, 95% CI 0.9-2.5) and 80% increased risk (OR=1.8, 95% CI 1.1-3.2), respectively, of follicular lymphoma (P for linear trend=0.05).

Data from a population-based case-control study conducted among women in Connecticut were used to evaluate the impact of cigarette smoking on the risk of NHL by histologic type, tumour grade, and immunologic type. A total of 601 histologically confirmed, incident cases of NHL and 718 population-based controls provided in-person interviews.

Then this

Diets high in fat and animal protein linked to increased risk of non-Hodgkin's lymphoma

.......The study was conducted between 1995 and 2001 on 601 Connecticut women between the ages of 21 and 84 diagnosed with varying subtypes of NHL. Using a Food Frequency Questionnaire (FFQ) developed by the Fred Hutchinson Cancer Research Center, each participant was asked to characterize her usual diet in the year prior to being interviewed. The FFQ collects consumption frequency and portion size data for approximately 120 foods and beverages and is periodically updated to reflect U.S. food consumption patterns and major market changes. After completion, the FFQ was sent to the Fred Hutchinson Cancer Research Center for calculating average daily nutrient intakes. The study included a control group of 717 women.

A *data dredge* with a *Trojan Number* of just 601 Connecticut women! They all involved Tongzhang Zheng, M.D., associate professor of epidemiology and environmental health at Yale School of Medicine. It out-Harvards Harvard!

Meanwhile, the body that had committed the biggest statistical fraud ever in its study of Environmental Tobacco Smoke, poured millions of dollars into the likes of the Harvard group, which brings us to –

EPA

It is the American way. When they are faced with a large problem such as being attacked or challenged for space supremacy, they set up an industry: so it was with pollution and cancer. On July 9, 1970, a Special Message was sent from the President to the Congress About Reorganization Plans to Establish the Environmental Protection Agency and the National Oceanic and Atmospheric

Administration. The new foundation subsumed the functions and, more importantly, the funding of many existing agencies. It had unparalleled powers of patronage over vast swathes of research and preparation of legislation. Nothing inherently wrong with that, of course, depending on how those powers were used. The problem was that the EPA was born on December 2nd that year out of the turmoil of hysteria that surrounded Rachel Carson's *Silent Spring*. In the EPA's own account of its history:

> *Silent Spring played in the history of environmentalism roughly the same role that Uncle Tom's Cabin played in the abolitionist movement. In fact, EPA today may be said without exaggeration to be the extended shadow of Rachel Carson. The influence of her book has brought together over 14,000 scientists, lawyers, managers, and other employees across the country to fight the good fight for "environmental protection."*

Silent Spring was a masterpiece of emotional propaganda, but as far as science was concerned, it was a work of subversion. Chief villain of Carson's book was DDT, claimed to be responsible for the decline of raptors. The futility of this claim is easily demonstrated by comparison with Canada with a lot of DDT but a lesser propensity to shoot everything that moves.

Of course there were very serious problems of pollution that needed to be tackled. Those of us old enough to remember the Great London Smog of December 1952, welcomed the UK Government's introduction of its first Clean Air Act in 1956, the effect of which was miraculous. In the early days of the EPA there were equal successes in the fight against pollution, the 1977 Clean Air Act Amendments for example, but in that burgeoning bureaucracy lurked the shadow of anti-science. This was not only in tune with the *Zeitgeist*, but was one of the main factors informing it.

During the 1980s the EPA began a programme of setting up a number of chimeras – dioxins (which have been shown to cause nothing other than the skin disease chloracne, and that only at high doses) PCBs, domestic radon (a proven non-hazard), even carbon dioxide, an essential to life on earth, and, of course, environmental tobacco smoke. There were numerous great and empty scares, such as the one involving Alar, based on feeding grotesque quantities to hapless tumour-prone rodents.

As the 1990s opened, the EPA changed its strategy. It would no longer work in reactive mode, but would actively pursue the reduction of *relative risk* in the environment. It set up the Relative Risk Reduction Strategies Committee and the search for accidental correlations was on.

There were two significant events in 1992-3. The EPA declared Environmental Tobacco Smoke (ETS) to be a human carcinogen. As we saw in chapter 13 this was based on the greatest statistical fraud ever. It was a watershed. Debased statistics had been circulating in epidemiological journals for some years, and had been exploited by the EPA, but now a major and powerful government agency was brazenly flaunting ludicrous statistical criteria (P<0.1 and RR=1.19) as an excuse for draconian legislation. Science would no longer be an impediment to political action. The second event was the appointment of Carol Browner as Agency Administrator. She was to become the longest serving holder of that post and had a close relationship with the Clinton-Gore White House. Under her tutelage political power would be the driving force in the Agency.

Let there be no mistake. The EPA kills people. In the 1970s it issued reports to the effect that chlorination of water at a concentration of 100 parts per billion was associated with a risk of cancer of one in 10,000. As a result the government of Peru stopped chlorinating. The consequent epidemic of cholera produced a million cases and 10,000 deaths. Via commercial air travel the epidemic spread round South America and the rate of infection in the USA increased tenfold. Finally, in 1992 the EPA's Science Advisory Board acknowledged that the link between chlorinated drinking water and cancer was not scientifically supportable.

On June 14, 1972, the Environmental Protection Agency's first Administrator, William Ruckelshaus, ignoring the advice of his scientific advisors, banned virtually all domestic uses of the pesticide DDT. Up to that point it had been regarded as the miracle chemical, conservatively estimated to have saved 100 million lives. It was virtually harmless to humans, requiring a huge dose to kill, but of course like everything else it produced tumours in specially bred tumour-prone rats at great concentrations. And then there was the Carson mythology that had given birth to the EPA. The Agency and its allies used their influence with international organisations to enforce the ban throughout the world. Some poor countries were actually blackmailed into banning it under threat of withdrawal of aid. As a result two and a half million people die of malaria every year, most of them poor children in Africa.

Asbestos is an invaluable material that has extraordinary resistance to heat, mechanical stress, and water. It is flexible and has low electrical conductivity. It is also resistant to acids and alkalis, making it useful in guarding against corrosion. One of the two forms, however, is deadly when inhaled in large concentrations (but so is water and about five million times faster) yet it has saved hundreds of thousands of lives. The EPA elected asbestos as one of its chimeras and targets. It exaggerated the risk of cancer from asbestos inhalation by at least a factor of ten. Like water, it was perfectly safe in the right place, but the EPA campaign triggered a tsunami of litigation that drove some 60 major companies to the wall and caused the virtual collapse of Lloyds of London. The World Trade Center Towers were designed to be protected by sprayed asbestos, but the precaution was omitted as a result of the anti-asbestos campaign. The inventor of the asbestos spray process, Herbert Levine, was distressed and predicted that "If a fire breaks out above the 64th floor that building will fall down." The insulation was designed to protect the building from collapse for four hours, which would have saved many lives. This resultant fire hazard was unnecessary. According to Harvard physics professor emeritus Richard Wilson no adverse health effect has ever been attributed to the Levine process.

Then there is the Challenger disaster, but enough is enough.

Tobacco wars

It was relatively easy to see off the likes of asbestos and DDT, even though they had been shown to save millions of lives. Tobacco was symbolic. It had become the evil icon of the PC movement. It had been shown that people were killing themselves by using it, but it was essential to establish that they were killing others too. The evidence, however, was just not there. The EPA could not achieve its ends by good science, so it bought bad science. One way the tobacco industry could fight back was to support sound science, which it did with great (but temporary) effect. It seemed like a good idea at the time, but the scientific era was coming to an end. The EPA and its allies adopted the *ad hominem* fallacy as its principal weapon. Anyone who said anything that appeared to support the tobacco case was simply in the pay of the industry and their arguments could be disregarded. Some of the finest minds in science, such as Fisher and Feinstein, had actually received tobacco money; so their scientific arguments, however sound, could be ignored. The industry, despite its wealth and power (perhaps, indeed, because of them) was vanquished. It was subjected to humiliating conditions by the courts. Totally irrational bans on public smoking started in the PC fastness of California and spread around the world.

There is no doubt about it – every study of passive smoking, if evaluated on the basis of statistical probity, shows that it is harmless; but probity had been jettisoned. It was a deeply symbolic and decisive moment in time. Once you could get the world to accept a relative risk of 1.19 at a significance level of 10%, you could prove that anything caused anything. The scientific era that had started with Bacon four centuries earlier had come to an end and the world was ready to return to the rule of mumbo-jumbo. Here is the conclusion drawn by David H Root in a paper in *Risk Analysis* (Vol 23, No 4, 2003, pp 663-668, *Bacon, Boole, the EPA and Scientific Standards*):

> In the EPA report, there is the language and appearance of the logic of the physical sciences, but the substance of that logic has been replaced by the logic of the courtroom. The substitution is hardly noticeable, because the logic of the courtroom is so familiar, one does not note that it is out of place, and the logic of the physical sciences is not familiar so one does not mark its absence. Also, the probability calculations do not seem strange to the reader because he is ignorant of the data and may easily overlook the fact that his ignorance was not shared by the authors of the report at the time they wrote their hypotheses and selected their data.

The method suggested by Bacon is strange and awkward, but it has shown itself to be of value. It has spread far in the last 400 years, but it has not yet been adopted by the EPA. By relying on the logic of the courtroom rather than the logic of the physical sciences, EPA scientists are, to a practical degree, able to decide what is true, instead of being able only to discover what is true.

CDC

The "Communicable Disease Center," or CDC, opened in 1946 in the former Office of Malaria Control in War Areas in downtown Atlanta. Part of the U.S. Public Health Service (PHS), the CDC had a mission to work with state and local health officials in the fight against malaria (still prevalent in several Southern states), typhus and other communicable diseases. In 1947 it moved to its present headquarters in Atlanta. The Centers for Disease Control as it became known in the seventies did some wonderful work throughout the fifties, sixties and seventies, playing a major part in the eradication of diseases such as polio and smallpox throughout the world.

The CDC was so successful that it almost did itself out of a job. Apart from the occasional scare that it had to deal with, such as anthrax and West Nile disease, its traditional workload was much diminished. It is unclear whether this was a factor in its embracing of the new epidemiology, but it did so with enthusiasm.

The CDC became famous for its virtual body counts. Obesity, for example, which is the newest fashionable bugbear, is now claimed to kill 300,000 a year. Naturally tobacco was in for it and its body count was announced to be 400,000 a year. This number is a total fabrication – see, for example, the article *Lies, damned lies and 400,000 smoking-related deaths* by Levy and Marimont, *Regulation*, Vol 21 No 4 1988. The calculation involves almost every fiddle in the book. These include unacceptable risk ratios, substantial confounding factors, self-reporting, unrepresentative sample populations and many others. Most startling of all is that 60% of the "premature" deaths occurred at ages over seventy and 17% of them at eighty-five and above. It has been pointed out that the same data can be used to "prove" that tobacco saves 200,000 lives a year. The British zealots took the number, added fifty percent and adjusted pro rata for population and came up with 120,000, a statistic that is repeated *ad nauseam* without any attempt at justification.

EU

The European Union has been one of the great disappointments of our time. It was supposed to be the great democratic movement that would unite the war-ravaged continent in a new age of peace and progress. Instead it turned out to be an undemocratic sleazy empire, so riddled with corruption and fraud that it cannot even produce a set of audited accounts. It is a vast gravy train in which politicians, bureaucrats and hangers-on cream off the huge sums of money extorted from taxpayers. The worst aspect of all is that it is run by a group of unelected commissioners who exercise unprecedented powers. Naturally, the Green movement seized the environmental portfolio. It is graced by the unelected commissar for the environment, Margot Wallström, who celebrates her Green policies (i.e. a characteristic combination of ignorance and arrogance) in her own web site. She actually believes, for example, that the Greenhouse Effect, which is crucial to the very existence of life on earth, poses a threat to humanity. She boasts that:

> *"The EU now has more than 200 legal acts covering nearly all areas of the environment. About 40% of all infringement proceedings brought against Member States are concerned with the environment.*
>
> *I am convinced that stringent environmental targets in this area will be of benefit to all, and not least to the competitiveness of European industry. Some companies have already realised the advantages of environment-friendly production: they benefit from lower costs and new markets, consumers have less waste to dispose of, everybody gets a better environment."*

The sort of advantage she is talking about arises from fining UK electronics companies £6bn a year to recycle equipment manufactured by their rivals in low labour cost areas, hence producing a benefit of lower costs.

Taking her cue from California, the Dark State of Insanity, she banned hundreds of chemicals for no particular reason, cutting swathes through whole industries and leaving people like allotment holders with no protection against pests and diseases. The so-called REACH Directive, which comprises a monstrous 1,200 pages of the most opaque EU gobbledygook, threatens the very existence of a £34 billion a year enterprise. Here is an example quoted by crusading journalist Christopher Booker:

> *The consequences can be see from how the directive would impact on Gabriel-Chemie, an Austrian-owned firm independently run by Greg Hammond in Paddock Wood, Kent, with 50 employees. Mr Hammond's expertise is producing new colours for plastics, for customers such as Marks and Spencer, Sainsbury's, Tesco and Boots. Each week he may be asked to come up with 50 new colour compounds, often used in small quantities for just one specific purpose. His competitive edge lies in his chemical formulations, which remain commercially secret. Under REACH he would not only have to register each of 250-odd chemicals he uses, but also publicly disclose each formulation, so they would be instantly accessible to potential competitors, such as those from China already active in his market.*
>
> *Like thousands of others, the more Mr Hammond assesses the implications of REACH the more alarmed he becomes. Not only will he have to hire extra staff to cope with the paperwork. His greatest fear is that, by laying bare his trade secrets, his business could soon vanish overseas, closing him down, because not the least absurd feature of REACH is that it will not apply to products imported into the EU. By imposing such colossal costs on*

*one of the chief centres of the world's chemical industry, the EU could thus
be writing its suicide note.*

*No country has more to lose than Britain, whose chemical business has in
recent years been growing at six times the rate of Germany's, its nearest
European competitor. But the fact that this directive stems from a UK
initiative means there is little our Government can now do to prevent the
slow destruction of our last world-beating manufacturing industry. How
those Chinese must be laughing.*

For chemicals to be approved they have to go through a testing regime that is so
expensive that few companies can afford it; you know by now, the ritual sacrifice of
thousands of rodents on the altar of epidemiology. It was only a matter of time
before the first great plague of Europe occurred (Margot's murrains) and it struck
turkeys just before Christmas 2003 with blackhead (*Histomanos meleagridis*). She
had banned the only drug (Emtryl) that was effective, on the grounds that it was
"linked" with cancer in humans.

6 million is the number of animals required to be slaughtered in Mad Margot's
massacre and British politicians only noticed late in the day. **Fury at EU call for
'needless' chemical tests on animals** was the *Sunday Telegraph* headline in March
2004. The tests will be absolutely meaningless, since they are based on the
concentration fallacy, and most of the chemicals have been safely in use and tested
by industry and governments for decades. The EU REACH directive, which was the
last laugh for Michael Meacher, Britain's embarrassing former Environmental
Minister, also put a bomb under one of Britain's few remaining successful
manufacturing industries. Whom the gods would destroy...

The EU is puzzled that its economy is faltering compared with the rest of the world.
You can put some of it down to the Central Bank, but much of the rest is down to
the unelected power of the Green movement.

The Green Organisations
There is a whole network of organisations parading under the Green banner. The
main objective appears to be to return humanity to the New Stone Age. Every
technological advance, past and present, is a potential target, from the motorcar to
genetically engineered food crops. The movement is one of bewildering
complexity, with a huge web of inter-related connections and flow of funds.
According to the Internal Revenue Service, the total annual income of the top
twelve environmental pressure groups in the USA is $2 billion.

Greenpeace
In order to understand Greenpeace it is first necessary to appreciate that it is a very
large corporation. It has an international membership of 5 million with offices in 20
countries. Centred on Amsterdam, its global empire has been valued at £360
million. Like all corporations its main preoccupation is with cash flow. It has

mouths to feed and premises to run. In order to maintain this cash flow it needs to manufacture more and more of its product, which is anxiety. In the search for product it has to spread its activities into new fields and make more and more preposterous claims.

Greenpeace was founded in 1969 by about a dozen activists in the basement of a Unitarian Church in Vancouver, where a group of American draft dodgers had settled. Within 7 years, the organization was established in over twenty-five countries and had a $100 million budget. One of these activists was Patrick Moore, who later broke with the group and became one of its sternest critics. In March 2000, he described the group in *Oregon Wheat* magazine as "anti-human, anti-technology and anti-science, anti-organization and pro-anarchy, anti-trade, anti-free-enterprise, anti-democratic and basically anti-civilization." In October 2001, he added: "I had no idea that after I left in 1986 they would evolve into a band of scientific illiterates.... Clearly, my former Greenpeace colleagues are either not reading the morning paper or simply don't care about the truth."

Friends of the Earth

This is another vast international organisation. It specialises in harnessing the idealism of young people. The International group is funded by subscriptions from 68 national groups. The 2002 General Meeting in the Swiss mountains identified five priority campaigns for the network in the coming period: Climate Change; Genetically-Modified Organisms; Trade; Corporates; and International Financial Institutions. Much of its literature reads like the communist manifesto with an extra bit of misanthropy thrown in. For example, it forcefully promotes the DDT ban while disregarding the millions of deaths in Africa that have been the result.

The rest

The movement is one of inscrutable complexity. There is a web site (http://www.activistcash.com) that attempts to unravel some of the interconnections between the organisations (well over forty of them), the foundations and the celebrities.

The trademark of the Green movement is its enthusiastic espousal of criminality. Arson, piracy, criminal damage, threats and violence are all part of its repertoire. It is funded with remarkable generosity by various wealthy foundations (e.g. $1.4 million from the Turner Foundation and $0.7 million from the Rockefeller Brothers Fund to Greenpeace) and more scandalously by governments such as the EU. Its links with epidemiology are tenuous. It quotes results when they are convenient, but in general it is so unconcerned about scientific truth that now it does not bother even with the debased forms of statistics.

The Green organisations are so wealthy that they can afford to take a patrician attitude to the law. They ignore it when it is inconvenient and use it when it suits. Thus when a Scottish newspaper suggested that wealthy organic farmers, who went on a rampage of criminal damage on other farmers' crops, might have a vested interest, it was sued for libel and was obliged to make an out of court settlement.

BMA

Le Fanu has given a graphic account in his landmark book *The rise and fall of modern medicine* of how medical practice has drifted away from the scientific method. In the case of the British Medical Association the drift became a veritable stampede. At the head of this was a group of politically correct anti-tobacco zealots who produce report after report claiming that tobacco, and particularly passive smoking, was responsible for almost every ailment under the sun, naturally followed by a demand for a ban on smoking in public places. This culminated in a 74 page report issued in February 2004, along with another on obesity, which dealt with **Smoking and reproductive life**. Designed to hit the headlines, which it did most successfully, it is a turgid document, available on the web, and is nothing less than a celebratory festival of junk science. It is full of the sort of debased statistics we have seen over and over again in these pages, random correlations as causations, *weasel words* (*may, might, could* etc.) and, of course, ludicrous *relative risks* (e.g. **1.11** and **1.14**). It was in the appendix, however, that something much more **sinister and disturbing** appeared. It purported to be a listing of seven commandments that Sir Austin Bradford Hill had delivered as the guide to proper practice in epidemiology. The original nine were listed in chapter 13. Two of them (specificity and analogy) were simply omitted, but there were unsubtle additions to five of the others that actually contrived to reverse the meaning. Here is the BMA version of the seven remaining commandments with the additions emphasised:

Appendix A: Assessment of causality

Assessment of the relationship between and exposure and a particular outcome is made on the balance of all the available evidence. Sir Austin Bradford-Hill proposed several considerations to be taken into account, which have been widely used and adapted. Some key considerations follow.

Strength of the association

Strong associations are more likely to be causal than weak ones. Weak associations are more likely to be explained by undetected biases. ***However, this does not rule out the possibility of a weak association being causal.***

Consistency of the association

An association is more likely to be causal when a number of similar results emerge from different studies done in different populations. ***Lack of consistency, however, does not rule out a causal association.***

Temporality

For an exposure to cause an outcome, it must precede the effect.

Plausibility

Is there a biologically plausible mechanism by which the exposure could cause the outcome? The existence of a plausible mechanism may strengthen the evidence for causality; **however, lack of such a mechanism may simply reflect limitations in the current state of knowledge.**

Biological gradient

The observation that an increasing dose of an exposure increases the risk of an outcome strengthens the evidence for causality. **Again, however, absence of a dose-response does not rule out a causal association.**

Coherence

Coherence implies that the association does not conflict with current knowledge about the outcome.

Experimental evidence

Experimental studies in which changing the level of an exposure is found to change the risk of an outcome provide strong evidence for causality. **Such studies may not, however, always be possible, for practical or ethical reasons.**

Anyone who got as far as reading to the bottom of the list might have found something familiar in the way the BMA reversed the meaning of Bradford Hill's seven rules by a process of addition. Here is why:

Benjamin felt a nose nuzzling at his shoulder. He looked round. It was Clover. Her old eyes looked dimmer than ever. Without saying anything, she tugged gently at his mane and led him round to the end of the big barn, where the Seven Commandments were written. For a minute or two they stood gazing at the tatted wall with its white lettering.

'My sight is failing,' she said finally. 'Even when I was young I could not have read what was written there. But it appears to me that that wall looks different. Are the Seven Commandments the same as they used to be, Benjamin?'

For once Benjamin consented to break his rule, and he read out to her what was written on the wall. There was nothing there now except a single Commandment. It ran:

ALL ANIMALS ARE EQUAL
BUT SOME ANIMALS ARE MORE EQUAL THAN OTHERS

After that it did not seem strange when next day the pigs who were supervising the work of the farm all carried whips in their trotters. It did not seem strange to learn that the pigs had bought themselves a wireless set, were arranging to install a telephone, and had taken out subscriptions to John Bull, TitBits, *and the* Daily Mirror. *It did not seem strange when Napoleon was seen strolling in the farmhouse garden with a pipe in his mouth - no, not even when the pigs took Mr. Jones's clothes out of the wardrobes and put them on, Napoleon himself appearing in a black coat, ratcatcher breeches, and leather leggings, while his favourite sow appeared in the watered silk dress which Mrs. Jones had been used to wear on Sundays.*

Yes, it was one of those Orwell moments, increasingly frequent and increasingly chilling. Apart from the disgraceful contempt shown for science, how dare they produce such a travesty of the work of a great man? How can one of the foremost professional organisations sink so low?

A month later the same organisation was calling for draconian increases in the taxation on alcohol, preserving its pleasures for the relatively rich (such as doctors) while denying them to *hoi polloi*. The poor obviously cannot be trusted with such a dangerous substance (not like us, eh?).

The little league

The greatest claimants to the Harvard crown are the researchers of Tulane University, but they still have a long way to go. In 1997 a group of six of them formally withdrew a 1996 paper claiming that pesticides in combination had **1600** times the effect as environmental estrogens than the individual pesticides tested alone. The original paper generated enormous publicity. *Science* magazine, for example, not only published the study, but also ran a news item and an editorial about it. Lynn Goldman, head of the U.S. Environmental Protection Agency's Office of Prevention, Pesticides and Toxic Substances was quoted as saying that the Tulane findings could have "enormous policy implications" for EPA. The objections of sceptics were swept aside, but attempts by other workers to reproduce the results failed and the claims were buried, relatively quietly.

OK, anyone can make a mistake, and that is part of how science works, but within two months of *Science*'s commercial for the Tulane research, Congress had enacted the Food Quality Protection Act of 1996. Relying on the Tulane research, the new law required EPA to develop screening tests for pesticides that might have estrogenic properties. This is far from the first time that the name Tulane has been connected with dubious published results. A "metastudy" in 1999 produced a *relative risk* of **1.25** for a connection between passive smoking and heart attacks. Another remarkably poor study provided evidence for the claimants over breast implants. The list goes on.

But, of course, every major university and more than a few minor ones have departments of epidemiology or related subjects. They nearly all adhere to similar statistical standards. Even a cursory summary of them would be encyclopaedic, so here is a random selection in random order.

Oxford is the oldest English-speaking university in the world. Teaching was going on there in 1096. Despite recent decades of underfunding, it is still a major force in world science. Among the hundreds of famous names was John Locke, whom we met in chapter six as a student of cause and effect. Anyway, it was at Oxford that Dr. Michael F. G. Murphy and his "team" came up with an observation of such mind-blowing banality and inconsequence that it merits some sort of award. The headline from Reuters, which was seized upon by the world media, proclaimed **Childhood cancer less common in twins,** but the details of the story are well worth a browse by any aficionado of scientific garbage. The claim of a 20% shortfall of cancer in twins was based on their observation that their sample only produced fifteen cases, when in comparison with the general population they expected nineteen. According to Poisson, the observation is about one standard deviation away from the expectation, just about what you would expect.

The foundation stone for the University of Edinburgh was laid in 1789. Many are the great names associated with it, such as David Hume and Joseph Lister, but in modern times it is known for such achievements as "proving" that smoking causes meningitis. Edinburgh is the place where they keep the national figures for vCJD. In December 2001 I wrote the following comment:

> *Their web pages are full of lovely statistics based on very small numbers. Look at the death rate, for example. They tell us that the underlying trend is an increase by a factor of 1.27 a year (i.e. an exponential model) so that next year's deaths are predicted to total 35. Why stop at one year? On this model everyone in the UK will be dead within 60 years. Only a nasty old cynic would suggest that a curve other than the exponential could be fitted to these data. He might, for example, posit a wholly random (Poisson) distribution, perhaps modified by failures of diagnosis in the earlier years; or even a trend that was rising and is now falling. A data set of only about a hundred deaths in six years lends itself to almost any interpretation. As with other areas of modern academic life (such as climate research) a major factor is possibly where the next grant is coming from. A rising trend means future employment.*

Well, as it turned out the figure for the following year was 17 and the year after 18. Oddly enough, the model changed to a quadratic one in which the epidemic had reached its peak and was declining.

The University of Glasgow was established in 1451 and is the second oldest in Scotland. Readers of *Sorry, wrong number!* might remember them from the tale of *Return of the Magnificent Seven* in which a scare about "heavy" drinking and strokes turned out to be based on an excess of just seven deaths, which were part of a data dredge. A shock for those who thought that nitrates were the excessive fares charged by cab drivers out of hours occurred when researchers at Glasgow University claimed that nitrates in vegetables **could** be the cause of a rise in cancer of the gullet – or, on a closer reading of the story, the researchers have formed a hypothesis that they aimed to test with the aid of a chunk of taxpayers' money.

Back to the other side of the pond and the University of Michigan – **Men carrying pollutant have more boys** yelled the headline. Even the *Trojan Number* was a mere 208 children. The *Journal of Occupational and Environmental Medicine* actually printed this guff as a paper. Not only was this one of the most egregious bits of statistical nonsense to appear for some months, it was a serious case of lese-majesty. These upstarts obviously don't understand the pecking order, since, as reported in *Sorry, wrong number!* the great Devra Davis on April Fools Day 1998 "proved" that pollution produces more girls. The numbers in this "study" are so ineffably crass that they are not even worth the effort of analysing. It is all a fine example of the abuse of ratios, as we discussed in chapter 7.

"Smoking at work costs 35 million working days a year in absenteeism and that is simply among workers who smoke. This important and timely research suggests everybody has a lot to gain from workplace bans"(*The Daily Mail*). All this based on a classical piece of junk science from the University of Athens. It involved a sample of **no fewer than 30** teenagers and had all of the characteristics of the genre – self-reporting, no believable mechanism and, of course, no numbers to put to the statistical test.

A number watcher in the other Washington spotted what could be the record low for a claimed relative risk. The honour goes to *The Seattle Times* and University of Washington scientists. The study claimed a relative risk of **1.02** for death due to stagnant air. The whole thing is an absolute classic, from the impressive *Trojan Number* down to the final propaganda message that was a total non sequitur.

Several regular number watchers spotted another one, which appeared in most papers and, of course, the BBC. It came from researchers at the Catholic University of Louvain. This time asthma was blamed on the chlorine in swimming pools. Of course, childhood allergies have been ascribed to almost everything. In *Sorry, wrong number!* a study from Munich is quoted that claims childhood allergies are all down to margarine or, to be more accurate, one component of it, linoleic acid. Correspondents commented on a number of features in this study, such as the use of a proxy, some small numbers compared with the Trojan one, overcooking of some sparse numbers and a separate data dredge. It does, however, offer an interesting illustration of our remarks on the dangers of linear trend fitting, with straight lines mysteriously fitted to totally random arrays of points.

Salmon scares migrate across the Atlantic. **Scottish salmon is full of cancer toxins** screamed *The Daily Telegraph* in January 2004, and that was one of the milder headlines. The three inch high front page headline in the Daily Mail advised only eating salmon once every four months. That hoary old scare was originally the copyright of Salmon Woman of Chapter 12 (Miriam Jacobs of Surrey University) back in January 2001, but the scaremongers at Indiana University are no respecters of priority. It has run again and again (as has its converse emphasising the benefits of oily fish). Of course, it depends on the concentration fallacy and all the old usual suspects such as dioxins, which, as we weary of saying, cause nothing in humans other than the skin condition chloracne.

Again, as we saw in Chapter 11, it really beggars belief, but the *Sunday Telegraph* devoted a whole broadsheet page to a story carrying the headline **Is your son at risk of heart disease? Look at his hands.** This was the work of the Finger Prince, Liverpool University's Dr John Manning. To become a media don the rule is to establish your gimmick, then plug it for all you are worth. Dr Manning's gimmick is to put two fingers up to science.

That month it was fingers. The next month fingers were out and legs were in. As we saw, that daft data dredge came from the University of Bristol, whence one Professor George Smith tolds us that short legs in men are associated with a propensity to diabetes and heart diseases. It was also "scientists" at the University of Bristol that produced the headline quoted in chapter 12:

How water on the brain can scupper quiz hopefuls

Or how about Pylon Man of Chapter 16:

> One of the world's leading experts on the effects of radiation believes electricity pylons have helped spread foot and mouth disease. David Henshaw, a professor of physics at Bristol University, says the high-voltage power lines make the virus even more virulent. He believes the virus, carried by the wind, is electrically charged by the power lines and so better able to "stick" to animals. The principle works in much the same way as static electricity just as a statically charged balloon sticks to clothing, so the statically charged foot and mouth virus adheres to animals...

From Bristol to Birmingham – **DVT study calls for an end to in-flight alcohol** yelled the headline in *The Times* travel section:

> The first study into deep vein thrombosis (DVT) to be done among regular business flyers has recommended that alcohol be banned on flights. Although the vast majority of passengers are now aware of the risks of developing thrombosis and consequently take more onboard exercise, one in four still refuses to cut down on drinking, says the survey, carried out by Birmingham University.

This is what now passes for research in Britain's nationalised universities. Any school kid could send out a questionnaire and group the results (many do). Let us hope that most of them would have more common sense than to headline a result that isn't there. All we have here is a few anecdotes about the in-flight habits of the 12% who answered a questionnaire, in response to a media scare that so far has yielded no substance. The anti-alcohol lobby is just part of the wave of political correctness that has swept through Britain's nationalised universities in the glow of having seen off tobacco.

So, there we have it. A pseudo research project, based on a media scare, that did not have anything to do with the real disease or the identification of causes, or anything else real for that matter, followed by the inevitable progression to a call for draconian Government action to limit the public's right to do anything that meets with PC disapproval. It is the sort of thing that gives non-sequiturs a bad name.

Finally one of my favourites, as it launched the Number Watch web site.

> *EVEN the most hardened Eurovision Song Contest cynic must surely take pity on Serafin Zubiri, this year's Spanish entrant.*
>
> *The pianist and vocalist has been doomed by scientists before he has had a chance to sing a single note at Stockholm on May 13. Mr Zubiri has been drawn at number 13 in the show - and that, according to a study into the chances of winning Eurovision, means he is at a serious disadvantage.*
>
> *Dr Richard Wiseman, a psychologist at the University of Hertfordshire, has discovered that songs at number 13 in the final do much worse than number 12 or 14. Although the reasons why 13 is so unlucky are unclear, the discovery sheds light on a few Eurovision mysteries - particularly the abysmal record of Norway.*
>
> *Since it entered the contest in 1960, it has been at 13 four times, including its infamous nil points of 1981. Dr Wiseman suspects that the curse of 13 is a self-fulfilling prophecy. The number is regarded as unlucky in most European countries and as entertainers tend to be superstitious, their performances could suffer, he said.*
>
> *Those at 13 have come bottom four times and second from bottom four times. Dr Wiseman said: "Only two countries have won the contest from the 13th position - Belgium in 1986 and Norway in 1985. Belgium is one of the few European countries to regard 13 as lucky."*

So, 13 won **only twice** in 45 years. Just how staggering are these numbers? How many times would we expect it to win? Without getting into the banalities of the contest itself, we can try some rough numbers. There are a couple of dozen countries in each final and the competition has been running for 45 years, so at random the average number of wins would be 45/24, which is about 1.9, or in round numbers 2. As for coming last (or indeed any rank) four times, we can calculate the probabilities using the Poisson distribution. The probability of four occurrences of any given rank then turns out to be 7.9%. Even an epidemiologist would blush at this level of significance.

Exactly four years later Professor Wiseman re-emerged. His latest foray into the higher reaches of scientific thought was covered by the BBC, recycling the *birth month fallacy*. **Is your birthday linked to luck?** asks the headline. Followed by **Are you born lucky? "Scientists" are trying to find out if your birthday determines how successful you are.** You could even participate in the experiment on line. The results caused a great splash in the media, but it took some of the deftest touches of graphic artists, exercising the skills of chartmanship, to create the illusion that they were significant.

And so it goes on. Some of the most distinguished institutions in academia have lent their glorious names to piffle. It is hard to believe, for example, that University College Hospital Medical School claims that left-handers are twice as likely to get inflammatory bowel disease as the rest of us. Hundreds of dedicated staff devote their lives to the care of patients and the advancement of medical science, yet this sort of stuff goes out in their name. It is fashionable to have a department of epidemiology and it is guaranteed lots of Government grants and media attention. You might regard it all as a bit of harmless fun, like The Stars that people turn to when they open their tabloid newspapers, but it also frightens people and gives bureaucrats the excuse to bully them. Furthermore, it diverts resources that could have been used to advance real science and medicine.

18. Conclusion

*If we bring a little misery into your humdrum lives, it makes us feel as if our
hard work ain't been in vain for nothing.*
Paraphrased from Lina Lamont

Several correspondents have been kind enough to commend the wit in the
predecessor to this book. They will have been, perhaps, disappointed to find less
wit and more anger in this one. There has been much editing, indeed savaging, of
the content. However, one bit of marginal statistical chicanery is very much like
another and an endless litany of claims based on dubious estimates of risk would
be even more boring than what you have read so far. The insouciance with which
the new generation of "scientists" exploits the fears of the populace in order to
generate a publication, or more importantly in the modern age a headline, is a
cause for sadness rather than humour. There is something disturbingly
reprehensible about the willingness of a few people to exploit the anxieties of the
vulnerable, such as prospective parents.

We live in the post-scientific age. Science is not unique in experiencing a reverse.
In art, the products of geniuses such as Constable, Rodin, Picasso or Dali have been
superseded by piles of bricks, dead animals and unmade beds. In philosophy, the
post-modernists openly trade arrant nonsense in inflated journals under the
inspiration of charlatans such as Jacques Derrida. Similar trends have overwhelmed
most of the other academic disciplines, including History and English Literature.

Departments of Physics, those few that remain to practise the most central of
sciences, stand almost unpopulated by students or offer debased undemanding
courses; likewise mathematics. Institutions calling themselves universities offer
degrees in such subjects as media studies and golf course management.
Departments of theology have been closing down and the human need for faith is
now served by the new eco-theologians.

The turning point

When did the change take place? In what was intended to be the final draft of
Sorry, wrong number! in 1999, the turning point was placed fairly precisely at
1982. Then James Le Fanu's monumental work *The rise and fall of modern
medicine* came out. Not only did this require a hasty redraft of *Sorry*, but he had
arrived independently at exactly the same date.

So much happened in 1982 that was to change the future. In Britain, for example,
pass rates for school leaving examinations, which had been constant for decades,
began an inexorable rise of 1% a year that was still going on two decades later.
Words began to change their meaning ("professional", for example, which once
meant having served some sort of apprenticeship, now simply meant "paid").
Shaw's dictum that "all professions are conspiracies against the laity" became a
tenet of the governing philosophy. Bureaucrats, who had traditionally resisted

change, now began to see it as the reason for their existence. Scientists abandoned their tradition of scepticism and became believers. In the UK, Government interference in the running of universities, accompanied by savage funding cuts, became the norm. Morale dropped like a stone. In both Britain and the USA, conservatism had been abandoned by the new radical right wing governments, and meanwhile the new left was burrowing away at the institutions, in a movement that would ultimately bring it to power in both countries. As we saw in Chapter 5, McKeown's *The Role of Medicine* had now been out for three years and was dominating the argument in medical policy. *The causes of cancer* had been published the previous year.

In 1982, *The Medical Annual,* for the last time in a century of service to the profession, covered innovative moments in the development of medicine. Le Fanu writes:

> It was an honour to be invited by Sir Ronald to contribute to The Medical Annual, which, thanks to vigorous editing, was both lucid and informative. Its purpose was obviously to keep doctors 'up to date' but it has subsequently acquired the status of an important historical document, serving as a contemporaneous commentary on the major moments of post-war medicine as they unfolded.

> Then in 1983 the format of The Medical Annual suddenly changed. It no longer aspired to keep its readers up to date and at the cutting edge of medical ideas. Its contents became 'educational', directed primarily to General Practitioners and their trainees, with articles such as 'Patient Participation in General Practice' and 'Changing Behaviour – Smoking'. In this dreary and attenuated form it limped on for the next few years before finally expiring.

The new political movements of right and left actually had much in common. Behind a liberal façade, each evinced an implacable authoritarianism. In Britain the Thatcherites advanced a creed of TINA (there is no alternative), while in America the PC movement began to impose a harsh Orwellian control of language and behaviour. Such attitudes would not promote conditions under which real science could bloom.

The new eco-theologians borrowed from the old hard left by practising entryism. In fact, many of them were former communists who sought fresh woods and pastures new after the collapse of the Soviet Union. Where proportional representation gave them inordinate leverage, the Greens always bargained for the ministry of environment. It would be hard to find a media environmental correspondent who is not a fully paid up member of the movement. Above all, they gained power through the ostensibly neutral civil service. People like Sir Crispin Tickell, who has been credited with inventing the global warming scam, moved into the highest levels. He eventually became British Ambassador to the UN, but he exerted most power as advisor to Margaret Thatcher, urging her to exploit her uniqueness in being scientifically qualified to advance the cause in the world forum. This suited Thatcher, who was at war with the British coal miners and the Arab oil producers.

To claim that 1982 marked the turning point is not, of course, to say that much had not happened before that. It had been a decade since Richard Nixon declared his multi-billion dollar war on cancer, a war that was being lost. It has become a cliché that in the fog of war truth becomes the first casualty. Through its lax statistical methods the new epidemiology gave birth to a vast shoal of red herrings, diverting attention and, more importantly, funding away from the sciences that might provide a solution to the cancer threat. The billions of dollars allocated to Nixon's cancer war were largely frittered away on statistical frivolities.

The one in twenty lottery

The crucial argument is about levels of statistical significance. Whether it is stated as $P<0.05$ or C.I. at the 95% level, that is the level that is almost universal in epidemiology. In the media "statistically significant" has come to mean "with a one in twenty chance of being wrong", but it is almost never qualified. There is no doubt that the likes of Fisher and Hill would be horrified at the claims that are now being made on the basis of small, ill-controlled observational studies. There is a vast chasm between Fisher's little plots of land divided up into Graeco-Latin squares and the worldwide epidemiological industry in universities and other official institutions, all working on similar projects aimed at the approved targets. The calculation of level of significance is subject to assumptions made by authors, which might or might not be stated. Bayesians, of course, would argue that the one in twenty is really one in five or worse. Nevertheless, it is the sheer weight of numbers of epidemiologists that is the greatest factor in the production of nonsensical claims.

The proof of the pudding is in the eating. Whatever you think about any *a priori* arguments, the stark fact is that contradictions and absurdities of the sort quoted in the opening paragraph of this book abound. While journalists enthusiastically embrace every new scare story, people in pubs openly mock them. The "crisps cause cancer" scare was greeted with gales of laughter and had no impact on sales, while the "carcinogens in salmon" scare actually produced an increase in the sales of that commodity the following week. The tragedy is that it is Science as a whole that bears the odium. Most people are unaware that the word "epidemiologist" exists. What they read in their newspaper is what "The Scientists" say. As a result, science is held in low esteem throughout the "advanced" world. This is a tragedy not only for Science but also for humanity. Sometimes the tragedy is obvious, such as all those Peruvians dying needlessly of cholera. What is less obvious is the effect of diversion of support and resources away from the real science that has delivered unprecedented health to the population. Vapid epidemiological trials absorb billions of dollars that could have been devoted to, say, the biology of cell multiplication, which is most likely to give the clue to solving the dominating problem of cancer.

It is a mark of the arrogance of the practitioners of the cult of epidemiology that they assume that their footling trials can outdo decades, generations or even millennia of human experience. With three-quarters of the population, for example, using mobile phones without any prominent outbreak of an associated illness, they still promote their minuscule trials. Chemicals that have been used without significant problems by farmers and gardeners for years, even generations, are withdrawn because the manufacturers cannot afford the costs of sacrificing thousands of rodents on the altar of the new epidemiology. Activists urge bans for their own sake, without an iota of scientific evidence to support them, and they find a sympathetic ear in powerful people like the unelected European Commissioner for the Environment. The activists cannot stop, even if they wanted to, and each success has to be followed by a new campaign; for they have to maintain the cash flow of the large corporations that they have set up. They supply the targets and the epidemiologists supply the ammunition.

Causes and campaigns

People love a campaign. Give them a cause, meetings brimming with high emotion, demonstrations before television and newspaper cameras and their anonymous lives are suddenly filled with purpose. Threaten them with a harmless, if ugly, mobile phone antenna and they take to the streets. Meanwhile, they give their children their own mobile phones that, because of the inexorable workings of the inverse square law, expose them to a thousand times the signal amplitude (though still, of course, harmless). Teenagers and university students want to change the world and make it a better place than their parents managed; we all did. They are an easy target for ecological evangelists who have a glib and readily digested message. Their parents wanted to ban the bomb; they want to ban the insecticide, even if that does cause the death of millions of Africans. The extreme Greens want nothing less than a return to the New Stone Age. Whatever it is, they are against it. They exert undue influence in left-leaning parties and governments. Their campaigns, even the violent ones, receive a benign acquiescence that would have been startling just a generation ago.

The precautionary principle

Science fiction was once one of the most popular genres, but it has gone into decline. Most of it is poorly written and formulaic. Some stories were not well treated by subsequent intrusion of technological reality, like the one in which communication was lost because all the electronic vacuum tubes were smashed on crash landing on a remote planet. There are one or two, however, that probably seemed pretty ordinary at the time but now stand out as beacons of accurate prognostication. One such is a novella by Jack Williamson, published a year before *Nineteen Eighty Four*, entitled *With folded hands*. The protagonist is a small time businessman living on the edge, selling domestic robots. Suddenly ultra-efficient hominids appear from another planet. Not only do they make his rather dodgy business insolvent, but they take over the lives of himself and the rest of humanity.

They are all controlled by a central computer, which operates according to the **Prime Directive**: *to serve and obey, and guard men from harm.*

The deuteragonist is a rather seedy individual who actually invented the hominids and is now on the run while trying to find a way to destroy his creation. He fails and consents to have a brain operation to cure his "delusions". The hero, like the rest of humanity finds himself, with no interest in life, no work, no danger, no tension, no tools (and, of course, no tobacco or alcohol) and his every need looked after:

> *Stiff with terror, he made a weak and hollow laugh.*
> *'What is the matter, Mr. Underhill?' The alert mechanical must have perceived his shuddering illness. 'Are you unwell?'*
>
> *'No, there's nothing the matter with me,' he gasped desperately. 'Absolutely nothing! I've just found out that I'm perfectly happy under the Prime Directive. Everything is absolutely wonderful.' His voice came dry and hoarse and wild. 'You won't have to operate on me.'*
>
> *The car turned off the shining avenue, taking him back to the quiet splendour of his prison. His futile hands clenched and relaxed again, folded on his knees. There was nothing left to do.*

To understand the relevance of this parable to modern life, for the *Prime Directive* read *The Precautionary Principle* and for *the hominids* read the teeming bureaucrats that infest today's world.

The Precautionary Principle is much favoured by organisations like the EU under the urging of the likes of Greenpeace. It provides the excuse for implementing bans of things they don't like without having to muster any evidence. It is also an ideal cover for conducting trade wars. While it is sometimes possible to prove that a substance or process will produce a deleterious effect, it is not possible to prove that it will never do so.

The precautionary principle robs the new generation of the chance of a full life. Children are cocooned in their rooms with their computers and TV sets. Their playgrounds and sports fields have been closed down by personal injury lawyers and local politicians, sold off for housing estates. School expeditions are a thing of the past. Their parents fear the drunken drivers and paedophiles that lurk behind every corner. They are protected from all sorts of demons, most of them imaginary, and are now harangued for being fat.

Trivial pursuit

The progressive trivialisation of what now passes for academic research is now way beyond the bounds of reason. Two fabricated stories that reached the front pages of the posh dailies in mid-November 2003 illustrate only too well the climbing onto populist bandwagons that typifies the modern approach.

The Rugby Union World Cup had made the headlines for weeks, so two academics came up with an equation that hit the headlines, purporting to define the recipe for success in place kicking. It is total pseudo-mathematical balderdash. The terms are vague and undefinable, while there could not possibly be enough data to evaluate coefficients (so there aren't any). Some might argue that it is only a bit of harmless fun, but this is the same sort of stuff that promotes health scares and other social ills.

And "scientists" at the University of Central Lancashire hitched a ride on the coattails of a callipygous Australian chanteuse. This in *The Times*:

The science of Kylie's bottom
Kylie Minogue really does have the perfect bottom, according to scientists at Central Lancashire University. For the best behind, they say a woman should have a waist to hip ratio of 0.7. And for the perfect man? Never mind the backside, just measure the wallet.

How low can you go? A formula for the perfect slice of buttered toast? They did that one too. Meanwhile, serious developments that put ordinary people in real jeopardy occur almost without comment.

The turn of the century has been unique in the history of British health. For the first time ever it has actually started to decline. In the nation that gave birth to Joseph Lister and Florence Nightingale, one of the main causes of disease is unsanitary hospitals. Under the urging of the media, people panic about travelling abroad because of scares like the SARS outbreak, when one of the most dangerous places to find themselves in is a bed in their local hospital.

Half a century ago, when some of us oldies were children in hospital, there would be a regular inspection by Matron. She wore white gloves and would rub her fingers along arbitrary surfaces. Woe betide the ward sister if there was any trace of grime. Now the hospital is administered by a hierarchy of bureaucrats and the cleaning is farmed out to the firm that offers the lowest charge. Stories of grime, to say nothing of blood, pus, urine and faeces, are rife. Resistant forms of staphylococcus (MRSA) have established colonies in many hospital wards. Infection, particularly among children, is increasing steadily.

According to *The Times* in December 2002:

In 2000 the National Audit Office estimated that 100,000 infections a year are acquired in hospital, affecting nine per cent of patients at any one time. Many infections are due to antibiotic resistant superbugs such as MRSA; the incidence of MRSA has risen faster in Britain than anywhere else in Europe.
*These infections kill **5,000** people, contribute to a further 15,000 deaths and cost the NHS £1 billion a year. Up to 30 per cent of all acquired infections could be avoided with better handwashing and laundry practice, according*

to a National Audit Office report published this year. Good laundry practice is clearly an important part of infection control.........

Remember that this is in the nation that gave birth to Nightingale and Lister, and one that was invited to panic over a "calculated" 1,000 deaths from passive smoking. Real people are dying in their thousands, but the Government is too preoccupied with imaginary deaths to do anything about it. Millions are spent on hectoring the population about too much smoking, drinking and eating, while 300 people (and rising) every day are catching horrendous diseases in the government-controlled hospitals that are supposed to cure them.

The epidemiology of epidemiology

The big question is "Why do outbreaks of epidemiology occur?" It tends to break out whenever anything appears that is popular, scary or (heaven forefend) enjoyable. Day-to-day ailments, such as athlete's foot or acne, simply do not have the media pizzazz to satisfy the cravings of modern epidemiologists. They all want to be the next Hill and Doll. They want to be the ones who make one of the big breakthroughs. The unfortunate fact is that there ain't going to be any. If there were dramatic discoveries to be made, they would have been made by now, by virtue of the sheer pressure of numbers of epidemiologists around the world.

There is a sub-text in attacks on beneficial treatments such as HRT and it relates to the new Puritanism. The therapy actually makes many women feel better and enjoy life more. A puritan has been defined as one who lives in dread that someone somewhere might be enjoying life. Everything in life that is enjoyable carries risks and costs (football, alcohol, food, tobacco, sex etc.) What has changed is that ordinary people are no longer regarded by the establishment as being capable of making their own calculations of cost and benefit. The male version of HRT is even more reviled as a superficial indulgence, particularly by the majority of medical practitioners. Here is a prediction – as soon as male HRT becomes popular, epidemiologists will "prove" that it causes cancer.

So we are presented with a dilemma. There are no more dramatic epidemiological discoveries to be made, but there are thousands of epidemiologists who need to justify their existence. Fame is the spur. They have committed themselves to a career, possibly at the outset with some idealism. They have to pay their rent and feed their children. So what are they to do? What they do is recruit 2438 men from Wales or 601 women from Connecticut, pour them into a data dredge, and "prove" that short legs cause non-Hodgkin's Lymphoma. OK, so they have to trim a little here, fake a little there, bend the rules of statistical inference more than somewhat, but they get the vital publication in the *Journal of Epidemiology*. The University Public Relations Department is thrilled with the headline in the *Daily Trumpet*. They have the esteem of their peers. They get their tenure. God's in his heaven – all's right with the world.

The scare's the thing. There is nothing people enjoy more than a good fright, so long as it is in the comfort of their own homes and they can have a nice cup of tea when it is all over. "Ooh! Isn't it awful?" the old dears say as they prop their mammary glands on the garden fence, then go on to discuss Mrs Number Thirteen, who is no better than she should be. Fiction and reality have merged and it is difficult to tell them apart. Was it last night's soap or the penetrating documentary that established that eating salt causes terminal lumbago?

The dramatic developments in instrumentation mean that scares can be conjured out of next to nothing. We now know that there is a hole in the ozone layer, but how do we know there was not one before we developed the instruments? We can now detect parts per billion of any "contaminant" in food or the human body. The fact that it does not matter does not matter. Though there are no known effects at such dilutions of any non-living material, even the most potent poisons known to man, it is the story that counts.

Does size matter?

There is a device called a funnel plot. It is intended to demonstrate whether publication bias occurs in the study of a particular combination of putative cause and effect. It is constructed in the form of a scatter diagram with some measure of size of study plotted vertically and the relative risk horizontally. The idea is that, if there is no publication bias, the plot will take the form of an inverted conical funnel, i.e. an isosceles triangle surmounted by a narrow rectangle. The latter represents the very large properly conducted double blind trials that actually produce information. Now what this actually shows is that small studies serve no useful purpose at all. In fact, the implicit assumption in the whole idea of the funnel plot is that the results of small studies are so widely scattered that they tell us nothing. A paper in the BMJ (Eggar et al, 1997) gives several examples of symmetrical and asymmetrical funnel plots. It shows that in small studies of, for example, the use of beta-blockers in myocardial infarction, *relative risks* are claimed that range from 0.25 to 6. Now each of these extremes would normally be considered by epidemiologists to be highly significant, yet they point to two dramatically opposite conclusions.

Whether funnel plots actually demonstrate the occurrence of publication bias is rather an abstruse argument to rehearse here, but what they do show with great clarity is that small-scale observational epidemiological studies not only serve no useful function at all, they are positively harmful. The one large controlled and randomised study in the case of beta-blockers actually produced a *relative risk* close to unity.

Imagine two general practitioners in a small town. One reads an article that says beta-blockers reduce heart attacks to a quarter, the other reads that they increase heart attacks by a factor of six. Half the town are told to keep taking the tablets, while the other half are told to avoid them at all costs. The real truth is that they make no difference. This example encapsulates the problem that small, uncontrolled epidemiological studies create. Furthermore, the ordinary punters read the stories in their newspapers, or hear them yelled from their television sets and don't know whether they are coming or going. It is inconceivable that most science and health correspondents don't know what is going on, but they cannot resist the snappy and scary headline.

The small size of some studies beggars belief. The justification of the virtual body count in the British version of the salt scare was based on "well-controlled" studies of **19** and **79** patients and it claimed to have established a trend over three values of salt intake. **42** asthmatic children justified the poor parenting link, while **73** women were used to justify the pesticide and miscarriage scare. There are endless examples of studies on fewer than 200 people, only a small fraction of which we have mentioned on these pages. Many of them then divide that small number into groups in order to demonstrate a trend. Remember the problem in chapter 4 of determining whether a die is loaded with 100 throws? That was actually a simple question about a well-behaved test object, quite different from the complications of human beings and their diseases, yet it proved quite difficult. Grant dice the properties of anecdotalism, self-deception, forgetfulness, confounding factors, changeability, misguided helpfulness and sheer perverseness and a hundred throws is nowhere near enough.

Less research is needed

Occasionally we have come across the statement "More research is needed". If all the occurrences of this statement in the recent literature and media coverage were included, this book would have been the size of a telephone directory and filled to overflowing. What the statement really tells us is that the study is too small and ill-controlled to be useful. This is not to say that such studies are useless; it is worse than that. They are positively malign. We have conjectured in the section above that two medical practitioners could give opposite advice, depending on which account they had read. It might be that only one is right or, indeed, that both are wrong. The result could be much unnecessary suffering, anxiety and death. People give up a benign therapy because the media, ever hungry for a sensational scare story, have highlighted a research result that is, in fact, quite without meaning.

Then there is the starting point of all this, the contradictions and absurdities in paragraph one of this book, which are only a tiny selection of the totality. People become blasé. The researchers cry "wolf!" so often that when one does come people dismiss the possibility. In contrast, there are interested parties, who for some reason have got it in for some substance or form of behaviour, who will exploit such results and, by means of endless repetition, instil it into the public consciousness and particularly that of the dictators of the Nanny State. Above all, the reputation of science among the general population is diminished almost beyond repair.

So what is needed is not large numbers of small studies but a small number of large studies. They should be well-controlled and genuinely double blind. Above all, they should deal with the things that really matter, where the outcome could be a reduction in pain, anxiety and death.

Premature termination

One of the most dramatic events in the history of epidemiology was the termination of the Tamoxifen trial by American researchers. Here is the account of that event as recorded in *Sorry, wrong number!*:

> *Tamoxifen is a drug that was thought to be effective in the prevention of breast cancer. Trials were started in the USA by the National Cancer Institute. A British-led study, involving 4,500 women in Britain, Australia, New Zealand, Spain, Finland, Switzerland and Belgium was hoped to reach a total of 7,000 women, with the results not expected for several years. Suddenly the Americans stopped their trial and announced that tamoxifen reduced breast cancer by 45%. The scientists from the rest of the world were outraged. Not only had the Americans ruined the trial by "unblinding" it, but they demonstrated that they had been cheating all along – the whole point of a blind trial is that you do not know how the results are progressing, so that you cannot exercise any influence over them.*

> *Officials at the institute defended their decision to end the 6-year-old tamoxifen drug trial. According to Associated Press (April 7, 1998) Dr Leslie Ford said that the agency was following the standards set for the tamoxifen trial when it started. She said the trial was designed to ask whether tamoxifen could prevent breast cancer. "We all felt the question had been answered". She said a statistical evaluation showed that there was a clear difference in the incidence of breast cancer among women taking the drug compared to women who were not. Since half of the 13,388 women in the trial were getting placebo, the study was stopped so that all of them could benefit from the drug.*

> *"The Americans have unblinded the trial, which means it will be unbalanced and they will not be able to answer many questions," said Dr. Trevor Powles of the Royal Marsden Hospital, London. Powles, who in 1986 headed the first pilot study on the tamoxifen's supposed anti-carcinogenic effects, added "It looks as though the benefits of the drug are likely to substantially outweigh the risks, but it was too early to be sure. Dangers include an increased risk of getting endometrial cancer – cancer of the lining of the uterus – and blood clots in the lung."*

> *"You start to wonder what the hidden agenda is," said Michael Baum of University College Hospital, London, the other co-chairman of the British-led study. "Is the National Cancer Institute of America trying to defend its*

budget or something like that? And I don't think this is just sour grapes or British conservatism."

The fact is that we may now never know the benefits and dangers of this drug. Indeed, the British and Italian trials failed to confirm that there was any benefit at all. Shares in the British-based Zeneca Group, which produces the drug, rose immediately on the American announcement. It is yet another example of scientific publication by press conference. The people involved ought to be drummed out of whatever learned society they belong to.

That, unfortunately, was only the first of many such occurrences. Once the media get hold of them they are imbued with a greatly heightened drama. "Wow" thinks the general public "if they abandoned the trial it must be serious!"

A trial, if well designed, is prescribed to run for a certain length of time, in order to achieve results of an acceptable significance. It should be double blind, so that neither the researchers nor the participants know who is taking the treatment and who is taking the placebo. Of course, in some cases, such as HRT, it ought to be pretty obvious to the physician if not to the patient whether they are on it or not.

The concept does not really allow for some higher authority to be monitoring the progress waiting to descend *deus ex machina* to bring the whole caboodle to a halt.

The policy of cancelling arouses a number of concerns. First, there are security worries. Do we really believe in the efficacy of those "Chinese walls" that are supposed to stop different departments in financial institutions from leaking information to each other? Are there no innuendoes exchanged in the lap-dancing clubs after work? Second, the progress of such a trial in terms of, say, *relative risk* is a random walk, wandering up and down but, if the trial is long enough, gradually settling down to an equilibrium value. If it is terminated before that equilibrium is reached, can the result be regarded as significant? Would the trend have drifted the other way given time? Third, who prescribes the standards by which the action to terminate will be judged? It is rather disturbing that in at least one case the terminating condition involved a 95% Confidence Interval that embraced the value of relative risk of 1.0, which means there is no effect. Fourth, the very act of termination endows a study with much greater significance than it would otherwise be granted. Following the 2004 announcement of the termination of a Scandinavian HRT and breast cancer trial, the headline was **Breast cancer fears force doctors to axe second trial**. Yet this trial involved a mere 174 women. Furthermore, it was formed from the combination of two trials, one of which was producing "evidence" that HRT **protected** against cancer. Fifth, the whole thing involves the extreme value fallacy. If a dozen diseases are being monitored it only needs one of them to cross the arbitrary threshold for the trial to be terminated, yet for one of the others the treatment could have turned out to be wonderfully beneficial or devastatingly malign.

The next HRT trial was abandoned on the grounds of risk of stroke. Breast cancer did not figure. By April 2004, more than half the women on HRT had abandoned it, when yet another study appeared, exonerating it.

Medical practitioners can, and do, argue that continuing a trial in the face of evidence of harm is in contravention of their Hippocratic oath. The basic problem is – what constitutes evidence? On the whole it would do less harm if the trial were not begun in the first place. Indeed, there is something to be said for the sentiment expressed by Ernest Rutherford that opened chapter 4. If the claimed benefit requires statistics, is it sufficient to be worth thinking about?

Correlation is not causation

Much of the argument in the research quoted here has been of the calibre of claiming that blue eyes cause fair hair (or vice versa). Often the claims of causation are patently absurd to almost everyone except the researchers and the media reporters, but equally often they convey serious or sinister implications. There are plenty of interested parties with axes to grind who are only too pleased to be able to cherry-pick among the contrasting claims for the ones that suit their cause. In the comparison of two random variables the correlation coefficient is **never** zero. The first question to be determined is whether it is far enough from zero to be significant, which is the case of epidemiology means resorting to the one-in-twenty lottery. Even if the correlation is deemed significant, however, that is not sufficient evidence to warrant a claim of causation. As we saw in chapter 6, this is a very difficult question indeed, yet one that is frequently and airily dismissed.

One of the favourite ruses is fitting straight lines to points on a graph. The mathematical method of least squares seems to work much in the same way as the human eye, in that it is only the points at the ends of the line that make a contribution. You look at the points scattered about on the graph and can see that they are more or less in the form of a fuzzy line, but surprisingly often, if you remove a couple of points from either end, the line becomes a blob. Points close to the origin exert a particularly powerful influence and the cholesterol myth, for example, depends heavily on the fact that the Japanese eat little fat and are rarely diagnosed with heart disease.

Much is often made of the assumption that the correlation is real. In many cases it is so tenuous as to be missing presumed dead. For example, the graph published by the British SIFs that purports to provide evidence to prop up the salt scare is just a random scatter of points with a straight line mysteriously drawn through them. Any engineering or physics student who produced such a construction would have his laboratory log book thrown at him. Yet on that shaky foundation an edifice of dubious logical links is constructed, culminating in a remarkably precise virtual body count. It is only the last figure that is used to lambaste the food industry and bewilder the credulous majority of the population. By any standards of conventional science salt is innocent of all charges, yet health gurus and

Government ministers harangue people over their enjoyment of this simple and essential commodity.

The new age of Luddism

On the night of 4th November 1811, in the little village of Bulwell, a group of men armed with hammers, axes and pistols marched to the home of a master weaver named Hollingsworth. They made a forcible entry and set about destroying half a dozen weaving machines that they found threatening to their trade. They called themselves the followers of General Ludd. There are various theories as to the origins of the name (apprentice Ned Ludd, one of the weaving machine smashers, or even King Lud, who gave his name to London town) but Luddism was to become a force in society for centuries to come. The original Luddite rebellion raged for three months and over a thousand machines were destroyed. Eventually some 15,000 troops were deployed and suspected Luddites were shot or transported to Australia (where their beliefs persist to this day). They failed to hold back the industrial revolution, which had two centuries of triumph, but they had planted the seeds of a movement that would come to be politically dominant in the Twenty First Century.

There is not one new technology that has failed to attract the attentions of doom-saying scaremongers of the post-scientific age. Mobile phones, genetic engineering, agricultural chemicals, various therapies etc. all came under attack. Often this was based on no evidence at all, but in many cases the debased statistical standards of the new epidemiology played a part. Even nanotechnology, little more than a hyped playground for fun-loving scientists, was verbally assaulted by no less a figure than the heir to the British throne, who had proved unable to distinguish between science fact and science fiction. In contrast, a whole range of quack therapies and nostrums were promoted by people in high places, including the said heir. The motto of the new age was *If it's new it must be bad*.

Envoi

So that's it; the story of a branch of medical science that went awry, yet somehow was more in tune with the *Zeitgeist* than science itself, whose age was coming to an end. It was a gold rush triggered by the discovery of one nugget. Trouble is, that was all there was. The throng of prospectors, including one of the original finders, were left scrabbling in the dust, turning up the occasional rock streaked with iron pyrites, fools gold. Yet there were fools aplenty, ripe to be parted with their money. The media, ever-hungry for a scary headline, the bureaucrats and politicians, always on the look-out for a stick with which to beat the public into submission, the new Green revolutionaries, eager for any excuse to drag mankind back to the Stone Age, were all only too keen to act as agents selling the dross to the unsuspecting punters. In the public mind the science that was able to compute exactly how many neutrinos were emitted per second by the sun was the same science that told them that left-handers were more likely to get bowel disease.

It has been a story with a rich cast of characters; the great leaders of history struck down by infectious diseases that would one day be conquered by scientific medicine, the lone doctor who saved thousands of lives and created a new branch of science by removing a pump handle, the greatest genius of mathematical statistics who got it wrong, the renegade medical professor whose specious theory turned medicine on its head and changed the world, plus a full supporting cast of thousands of workaday epidemiologists, all just about to find the philosopher's stone.

And it has been a success story. No other branch of science has made such an impact on the minds of ordinary people. It invades their newspapers and television programmes, provides the weaponry by which the Gauleiters of the Nanny State enforce its will on them and determines the medications that are forced on them.

Should the reader, at this late stage, harbour the opinion that all the foregoing represents the rantings of a lone crazed individual, here is a penultimate thought from Le Fanu and Feinstein:

> *Nonetheless, epidemiological studies are easy to perform – take one group of people with a disease, another without, compare their lives and any differences can then be plausibly implicated as 'the cause' – and thus rapidly filled the vacuum of ignorance. But, and this is the crucial point, the human organism is very resilient and therefore on* prima facie *grounds 'everyday life' is unlikely to provide the correct explanation. Rather, the associations that do emerge from these studies are likely to be weak and contradictory, to the considerable confusion of the public. And, argues Professor Alvin Feinstein, editor of the* Journal of Clinical Epidemiology, *a scientific discipline that generates such conflicting findings (coffee does, or does not, cause bladder cancer or congenital defects or heart disease; alcohol does, or does not, cause breast cancer; keeping pets is, or is not, associated with multiple sclerosis, and so on) can hardly be considered 'scientific' at all, as its methods of investigation must be so clearly unreliable. 'In other branches of science substantial distress would be evoked by a conflicting result...authorities would clamour for special conferences or workshops intended to identify the [methodological] defect and to institute suitable repairs. No such conferences and no such workshops have occurred.' Professor Feinstein's inside observations are so important as to merit elaboration. A scientist in any serious scientific discipline, such as genetics, would be in serious trouble if his fellow scientists were unable to confirm or replicate his claim to have found the gene for fatness. He would gain a reputation as being 'unreliable' and universities would be reluctant to employ him. This self-imposed insistence on rigorous methodology is however missing from contemporary epidemiology; indeed the most striking feature is the insouciance with which epidemiologists announce their findings, as if they do not expect*

anybody to take them seriously. It would, after all, be a very serious matter if drinking alcohol really did *cause breast cancer.*

Let us leave the last word to one of them, the Li declaration that sums up the difference between modern epidemiology and real science:

As epidemiologists, we should not feel weaker because we don't understand the mechanisms.

Bibliography

Sorry, wrong number! The abuse of measurement by John Brignell (Brignell Associates, 2000)

The rise and fall of modern medicine by James Le Fanu (Little Brown, 1999)

What Risk: science, politics and public health edited by Roger Bate (Butterworth Heinemann, 1997)

The cholesterol myths by Uffe Ravnskov (New Trends, 2000)

Damned lies and statistics by Joel Best (University of California Press, 2001)

The Magical Maze by Ian Stewart (Weidenfield & Nicolson, 1997)

Junk science judo: self defense against health scares and scams by Steve J Milloy, (Cato, 2001)

Malaria and the DDT story by Richard Tren and Roger Bate (IEA, 2001)

Probability, random variables and stochastic processes by Athanathios Papoulis (McGraw Hill, 1965)

The foundations of statistical inference by Savage et al (Methuen, 1962)

Warning signs by Alan Caruba (Merril, 2003)

Statistical snake oil: the use and abuse of significance test in science by Robert A J Matthews (ESEF, 1999)

Science under siege: how the environmental misinformation campaign is affecting our laws by Michael Fumento (William Morrow, 1966)

Not the foot and mouth report: everything Tony Blair didn't want you to know about the biggest blunder of his premiership (Private Eye special report, November 2001)

Web links are too volatile to print here, but a list is maintained at *www.numberwatch.co.uk/links.htm*. In this book much use has been made of the invaluable archive at *www.junkscience.com*.

Index